ACCREDITATION OF PHARMACY INSTITUTIONS (NBA)

I0563527

AS PER REVISED NORMS OF 2013

DR. S. B. BHISE

M. Pharm, Ph.D
Former Principal,
Government College of Pharmacy
Karad.
MAHARASHTRA.
and
Managing Director,
KLK-Consultants, Pune.

NIRALI PRAKASHAN™
ADVANCEMENT OF KNOWLEDGE

N1309

ACCREDITATION OF PHARMACY INSTITUTIONS (NBA)

ISBN 978-93-5164-500-9

First Edition : March 2015

©   : **Author**

Published By :
NIRALI PRAKASHAN
Abhyudaya Pragati, 1312, Shivaji Nagar,
Off J.M. Road, PUNE – 411005
Tel - (020) 25512336/37/39, Fax - (020) 25511379
Email : niralipune@pragationline.com

DISTRIBUTION CENTRES

PUNE

Nirali Prakashan
119, Budhwar Peth, Jogeshwari Mandir Lane
Pune 411002, Maharashtra
Tel : (020) 2445 2044, 66022708, Fax : (020) 2445 1538
Email : niralilocal@pragationline.com

Nirali Prakashan
S. No. 28/25, Dhyari,
Near Pari Company, Pune 411041
Tel : (020) 24690204Fax : (020) 24690316
Email : bookorder@pragationline.com

MUMBAI

Nirali Prakashan
385, S.V.P. Road, Rasdhara Co-op. Hsg. Society Ltd.,
Girgaum, Mumbai 400004, Maharashtra
Tel : (022) 2385 6339 / 2386 9976, Fax : (022) 2386 9976
Email : niralimumbai@pragationline.com

DISTRIBUTION BRANCHES

NAGPUR

Pratibha Book Distributors
Above Maratha Mandir, Shop No. 3, First Floor,
Rani Jhanshi Square, Sitabuldi, Nagpur 440012,
Maharashtra, Tel : (0712) 254 7129

BENGALURU

Pragati Book House
House No. 1, Sanjeevappa Lane, Avenue Road Cross,
Opp. Rice Church, Bengaluru – 560002.
Tel : (080) 64513344, 64513355,
Mob : 9880582331, 9845021552
Email:bharatsavla@yahoo.com

JALGAON

Nirali Prakashan
34, V. V. Golani Market, Navi Peth, Jalgaon 425001,
Maharashtra, Tel : (0257) 222 0395
Mob : 94234 91860

KOLHAPUR

Nirali Prakashan
New Mahadvar Road,
Kedar Plaza, 1st Floor Opp. IDBI Bank
Kolhapur 416 012, Maharashtra. Mob : 9850046155

CHENNAI

Pragati Books
9/1, Montieth Road, Behind Taas Mahal, Egmore,
Chennai 600008 Tamil Nadu, Tel : (044) 6518 3535,
Mob : 94440 01782 / 98450 21552 / 98805 82331, Email : bharatsavla@yahoo.com

RETAIL OUTLETS

PUNE

Pragati Book Centre
157, Budhwar Peth, Opp. Ratan Talkies,
Pune 411002, Maharashtra
Tel : (020) 2445 8887 / 6602 2707, Fax : (020) 2445 8887

Pragati Book Centre
Amber Chamber, 28/A, Budhwar Peth,
Appa Balwant Chowk, Pune : 411002, Maharashtra,
Tel : (020) 20240335 / 66281669
Email : pbcpune@pragationline.com

Pragati Book Centre
676/B, Budhwar Peth, Opp. Jogeshwari Mandir,
Pune 411002, Maharashtra
Tel : (020) 6601 7784 / 6602 0855

PBC Book Sellers & Stationers
152, Budhwar Peth, Pune 411002, Maharashtra
Tel : (020) 2445 2254 / 6609 2463

MUMBAI

Pragati Book Corner
Indira Niwas, 111 - A, Bhavani Shankar Road, Dadar (W), Mumbai 400028, Maharashtra
Tel : (022) 2422 3526 / 6662 5254, Email : pbcmumbai@pragationline.com

www.pragationline.com

info@pragationline.com

PREFACE

Since National Board of Accreditation (NBA) has revised the norms for accreditation, faculty from pharmaceutical sciences needs to be acquainted with the new content. At the same time comparison of Indian norms with global standards is desirable. Competencies for pharmacists have not been included in Indian curricula.

In order to meet all these objectives a book on **'Accrediation of Pharmacy Instituions'** is presented here.

I hope that readers will enrich the content by appropriate feedback.

PUNE
MARCH 2015

DR. S. B. BHISE

FOREWORD

With the opening of Indian economy, several service sectors, including education sector have undergone rapid metamorphasis. Full scale opening of education sector in the form of FDI in education has facilitated, establishment of campuses of foreign universities in India and reciprocal actions of competent Indian universities outside India. Accreditation of technical institutions in India has become a reality after India signing Washington accord in 2013. National Board of Accreditation (NBA), as an autonomous body, is monitoring the task of accreditation of technical institutions in India.

Due to signing of Washington accord, Indian accreditation criteria have changed to match the global accreditation process. The new criteria are outcome base The concepts of Program Educational Objectives, Program Outcomes, and Court Outcomes have been introduced. NBA has published a separate document for accreditation of Pharmacy institutions. Since all above mentioned concepts are new to the pharmacy faculty, discussions on them is extremely necessary.

All over the world, training in pharmacy is under the purview of health sciences. In USA, standards of accreditation have been developed by Accreditation Council for Pharmacy Education (ACPE). The guidelines and standards for the program of Pharm. D. have been published in 2007. Similarly, a sell' study guide for Continuing Education (CE) has been published. In addition, the International Forum for Quality Assurance of Pharmacy Education has published a booklet entitled, "A Global Framework for Quality Assurance of Pharmacy Education" in 2008. In the present book, all these documents have been reviewed by the author.

In the context of global documents, one cannot lose the sight of Indian scenario. Hence, one chapter on "Change of mindset" and another chapter on "What should be done in India ?" is a useful addition to the main text. Thus, the author of the boo exposes the readers both. to Indian and global scenario with equal effectiveness. I hope, that this book deserves to be on the desk of all stake-holders related to pharmacy education.

Pune
March 2015

PROF. (DR.) CHANDRAKANT KOKATE
VICE-CHANCELLOR, KLE UNIVERSITY, BELAGAVI,
FORMER PRESIDENT, PHARMACY COUNCIL OF INDIA,
FORMER VICE-CHANCELLOR, KAKATIYA UNIVERSITY, WARANGAL.

ACKNOWLEDGEMENTS

A book on Accreditation was planned for more than a year. Initially, I wrote three articles during 2014 in Indian Journal of Pharmaceutical Education and Research (IJPER) about accreditation. My co-author for two articles, Mr. Adwait Deshpande deserves compliments for helping me in the venture.

Secretarial assistance from Mr. Somnath Nalawade and partly Mrs. Seema Gawade is strongly appreciated for typing the manuscript.

My younger son, Suhas has been pressing for books for more than a year. The first book compliments him for his continued patience. Moral support and tactical help from my wife Manjiri, son Sourabh and daughter in law Abha need parallel app aud for bearing with my scattered books and papers throughout my residence.

Prof. S.B. Gokhale needs a special appreciation for pro-active support in accelerating publication of the book in shortest possible time.

I am thankful to Mr. Dineshbhai Furia, Mr. Jignesh Furia and Staff of Nirali Prakashan for their committed efforts in publishing the book.

PUNE
MARCH 2015

DR. S. B. BHISE

CONTENTS

Chapter 1

BACKGROUND AND NEW NORMS

From 1991, Indian economy has been globalized. It was a major political and economic decision with long-term consequences. Opening up of Indian economy to global players created a series of opportunities in other sectors. Education sector is awaiting full consequences of opening up even now. Foreign Direct Investment (FDI) in Education and opening of campuses to foreign universities is still awaited due to political reasons; however India has become signatory to Washington Accord in 2013 after getting provisional membership in 2007. As a result, robust, accountable and objective-based system of Accreditation of technical institutions has become a reality now. All components of technical education including Engineering & Technology, Pharmacy, Architecture, Management, Hotel Management & Catering Technology, Town & Country Planning, Applied Arts and Crafts have been covered for the purpose of Accreditation. The present book primarily concentrates on provisions for Pharmaceutical Sciences. Along with guidelines for Indian sector a global commentary has also been included in order to ensure that Indian pharmacists know how unique they are in global competition.

We all are well familiar with the word "Quality Assurance" in the context of drugs. Assurance of quality in the manufacture of drugs involves monitoring of quality of raw material and the process of formulation at every step so that the final product is of predefined quality. When the same concept is applied to the process of pharmacy education, the efforts related to "Quality Assurance of Pharmacy Education" are reflected in the process of accreditation. Quality assurance in Pharmacy education essentially means monitoring availability of 'Right' students and monitoring the process of effective teaching, learning practice in such a way that the trained graduate is useful to the needs of community as well as pharmaceutical industries. On international platform, few accredit ting agencies specially designed for pharmacy education have been established e.g. in USA, Accreditation Council for Pharmacy Education (ACPE) has provided standards and guidelines for pharmacy institutions desiring accreditation by ACPE. In years to come, accreditation is going to be mandatory for all institutions in India; hence knowing background about what accreditation is necessary.

Two national bodies are mainly involved in accreditation of institutes n India

- National Accreditation and Assessment Council (NAAC) and
- National Board of Accreditation (NBA)

NAAC was established by University Grants Commission (UGC) as an autonomous body and NBA was established under the umbrella of All India Council for Technical Education (AICTE) both in 1994. While purview of NAAC was quality assurance of education under university and colleges imparting higher education in areas other than technical education, the mandate of NBA was limited to diploma, degree and post-graduate institutions in Engineering, Technology, Pharmacy, Management, Architecture and related disciplines. Once a part of AICTE, NBA became autonomous on 7th January 2010.

NBA looks forward to be an accrediting agency of international repute by ensuring the highest degree of credibility in assurance of quality and relevance of professional education and fulfill the expectations of its stakeholders viz. academicians, corporate, educational institutions, government, industry, regulators, students and their parents.

NBA aims to achieve this by stimulating the quality of teaching, self evaluation, and accountability in the higher education system, which help institutions realize their academic objectives and adopt teaching practices that enables them to produce high-quality professions and to assess and accredit the programs offered by the colleges or the institutions, or both, imparting technical and professional education.

THE REVISION OF NORMS

NBA format and criteria for accreditation have been revised multiple times internally since January 2009 and the latest accepted criteria are prescribed in January 2013. One question may come up in reader's mind "What is the reason for revising the norms for accreditation?" The answer lies in the process of globalization. Along with globalization of Indian economy, the education sector is also getting globalized. To achieve uniformity in education, under the banner of International Engineering Alliance, three accords have been signed, The Washington Accord in 1989, The Sydney Accord in 2001 and The Dublin Accord in 2002. India has decided to get aligned with "Washington Accord (WA)".WA is an international agreement among the engineering quality assurance organizations of several countries. The signatories of the accord recognize that graduate accredited programs in any of the signatory countries be recognized by other countries having made the academic requirements for entry to the practice of engineering. The accord enables the signatory to have comparable criteria, policies and procedures for accrediting engineering programs. In India, degree pharmacy education comes under the purview of All India Council for Technical Education (AICTE). Before attaining the autonomous status, NBA was a subsidiary body of AICTE. Thus being under purview of AICTE, Pharmacy education in India obviously became party to NBA and the process of accreditation. As per WA, a country becomes eligible for full fledged membership after two years of provisional membership if all other members unanimously agree for the same. The NBA became a provisional member of the WA, on 20th June 2007. In 2008, India approached WA for full membership, but this bid to be a full member of WA was not acceded in 2009. However India's provisional membership was extended as a special case. This evoked the revision of accreditation format of NBA and thus accreditation format has been internally modified several times recently. In March 2012, World Summit on Accreditation was held in New Delhi and Pharmacy Council of India (PCI) was an active participant for the same. This summit was organized by NBA. Subsequently NBA criteria for accreditation were revised, latest being January 2013 version. Being a full-fledged member of WA ensures that undergraduate degree of a member country would be accorded an equal status in all other member countries. This is the reason why accreditation standards have been thoroughly revised.

Accreditation is a process of quality assurance and improvement, whereby a program in an institution is critically appraised to verify that the institution or the prcgram continues to meet and exceed the norms and standards prescribed by the appropriate designated authorities. In India, NBA is conferred to be the appropriate designrated authority. Accreditation does not seek to replace the system of award of degree and diplomas by the universities/ autonomous institutions. Thus accreditation is additional or complementary to the existing system of affiliation to the respective university. Accredtation provides assurance that the academic aims and objectives of the institution are honestly pursued, are effectively achieved by the resources available, and the institution has demonstrated capabilities of ensuring effectiveness of the educational programs over the validity period of accreditation. Thus, NBA accreditation is a quality assurance scheme for higher technical education in India.

CURRENT FORMAT OF NBA

The revised NBA standards work on two-tier system: Tier I and Tier II. While Tier document is for autonomous systems and university departments, Tier II document is for non autonomous institutions affiliated to universities. Spread of Pharmacy education in India is very limited in university departments or autonomous institutes while more than 95% of it is under the umbrella of non autonomous affiliated colleges. hence they are supposed to follow Tier II documents. However, there is no harm for any nor autonomous institutions to apply for Tier I document, if they feel that they are capable of following the criteria applicable to Tier I system.

Significance of accreditation and accreditation policy has been well described in Accreditation Manual for Pharmacy UG programs by NBA. Briefly, significance of accreditation lies in following parameters:

- Identifying weakness of the program and suggestions for improvement.
- Continuous improvement of quality of the program.
- To facilitate institutions for updating the program curriculum, teaching-learning process (TLP), faculty improvement and students' improvement.

- To excel among stakeholders.
- To attain international recognition.
- To facilitate the mobility of graduated students and professionals.

Salient features of accreditation policy are as follows:

- Programs, instead of educational institutions, are accredated at present.
- Programs which have trained graduates for at least two academic years will be considered for full accreditation.
- The institution desiring accreditation has to make a written request to NBA for accreditation and has to abide by the NBA's accreditation manual, rules and regulations.
- The program may be granted accreditation for a maximum period of 5 years.
- Programs will be assessed and evaluated in accordance with the accreditation criteria. Accreditation is based on satisfying the minimum standards.
- The educational institution, desiring NBA status shall bear the cost of accreditation.

There are 9 criteria for evaluation of the program. Tier I and Tier II marking systems differ only in few criteria. New accreditation format and process of NBA is based on objectives. This being distinct feature of current format, certain new terms have been introduced in the process. Reader should be aware of following terms.

- **Program Educational Objectives (PEOs):** These are broad statements that describe the career and professional accomplishments that the program is preparing graduates to achieve.
- **Program outcomes (POs):** These are narrower statements that describe what students are expected to know and be able to do upon the graduation.
- **Course outcomes (COs):** These are narrower statements that describe what students are expected to know, and be able to at the end of each course.
- **Assessment:** Assessment is one or more processes, carried out by the institutions that identify, collect and prepare data to evaluate the achievement of the PEOs and POs.
- **Evaluation:** Evaluation is one more process, done by the evaluation team for interpreting the data and evidence accumulated through assessment objectives. Evaluation determines the extent to which PEOs or POs are being achieved, and results in decisions and actions to improve the program.
- **Mapping:** Mapping is the process of representing, preferably in a matrix form, the correlation among the parameters. It may be done for one to many, many to one and many to many parameters.
- **Rubric:** A rubric articulates the expectations for students' performance. It is a set of criteria for assessing students' work or performance.

Few important points of these 9 criteria of the new accreditation process are discussed as follows.

Vision, Mission and Program Educational Objectives (PEOs) :

Vision is a futuristic statement that the institution would like to achieve over a long period of time and mission is the means by which it proposes to move towards the stated vision. Thus vision is a long-term goal and mission indicates short-term goals through which the institution can achieve the vision. e.g. If vision is established as "Life-long learning" then mission may be indicated as "Continuous professional education through short-term courses".

Program Educational Objectives (PEOs) are broad statements that describe the career and professional accomplishments that the program is preparing graduates to achieve.

e.g. "Practicing cGMPs" can be of the PEO for B.Pharm. program.

- PEOs is a new concept in the current accreditation process. Following points should be considered regarding PEOs –
- PEOs should be assessable and realistic within the context of the committed resources
- A comprehensive list of various stake-holders of the program involved in the process of defining and re-defining PEOs should be provided
- Following factors should be considered while designing PEOs –
- The PEOs should be consistent with the mission of the Institute.
- All stake holders should participate in the process of framing the PEOs.
- The number of PEOs should be manageable.
- PEOs should be based on the need of the stake-holders
- PEOs should be achievable by the program
- PEOs should be specific to the program and not too broad.
- PEOs should not be too narrow and similar to the POs.
- PEOs should be reviewed periodically based on the feedback of the program's various stake-holders.
- It is expected to indicate how the administrative system helps the program in ensuring the attainment of the PEOs. Necessary documentation should be maintained.

Program Outcomes (POs):

Program Outcomes (POs) are narrower statements that describe what students are expected to know and be able to do upon the graduation. These lead to the skills, knowledge, and behavior that students acquire in their program.

e.g. "Knowing regulatory aspects of cGMP" can be one of the program educational objectives of B.Pharm. program.

Graduates attributes (GAs) are a set of individually assessable outcomes that are the components indicative of the Graduate's potential to acquire competence to practice at the appropriate level. Following are the GAs identified by the NBA for a UG Pharmacy program –

- Pharmacy knowledge
- Thinking abilities
- Planning abilities
- Leadership skills
- Professional identity
- The Pharmacist and society
- Environment and sustainability
- Ethics
- Communications
- Modern tool usage
- Lifelong learning

The POs formulated for B. Pharm. must be consistent with the NBA's GAs of the UG Pharmacy program. The POs must be linked to the attainment of the POs. The attainment of POs may be assessed by direct and indirect methods. In case of in-direct assessment, "Rubric" is a new term used in the documents. A Rubric expresses the expectations for students' performance. It is a set of criteria for assessing students' work / performance. It is particularly suited to such POs which are complex or not easily quantifiable. Such POs may not have clear right or wrong answers, or which are not evaluated with the standardized tests or survey, e.g. Assessment of "critical thinking" will require Rubrics to be developed.

The results of assessment of each PO should be indicated. It is important in continuous improvement of the program. There should be a process of revising and redefining POs based on the needs of the stake-holders.

Program Curriculum :

Conventionally in the curriculum, titles of the subjects, sub-components involved along-with weightage in the form of marks or number of hours. Course objectives may not be clearly defined. While defining the curriculum for the purpose of accreditation, following points should be specially considered –

- The relevance of curriculum components including core pharmacy courses to the POs shall be given.

- It should be indicated how the core pharmacy subjects in curriculum lend the learning experience with the problem solving related to actual life.
- If the curriculum is not able to achieve POs / COs, then the gaps should be identified and additional training to be provided to bridge the gap.
- Required information for assessment, evaluation and review methods to evaluate attainment of COs be indicated.
- Course Outcomes COs are narrower statements that describe what students are expected to know, and be able to at the end of each course. These lead to skills, knowledge and behavior that students acquire in their program.
- e.g. "How to prepare tablets" can be one of the course objectives in the course entitled "Pharmaceutics".

Student's Performance in the Program:

Students admitted to the program should be capable of achieving the POs. the policies and procedure for admission should be transparent. Academic performance of the students be monitored carefully. The Institute should provide support services like counseling and should have a mechanism to redress problems of the students. Information about admission intake, success rate, academic performance, placement be provided for three complete academic years.

Faculty Contributions:

Adequate number of qualified faculty should be available. The faculty must be actively involved in research and development (R&D). The faculty must have academic freedom. They should be engaged in continuous improvement of PEOs and POs. following information about the faculty for three complete academic years be provided –

- Student – Teacher Ratio (STR)
- Faculty – Cadre Ratio (FCR)
- Faculty Qualifications (FQ)
- Faculty Retention (FR)
- Faculty Research Publications (FRP)
- Faculty Intellectual Property Rights (FIPR)
- Funded R&D Projects and Consultancy (FRDC)
- Faculty interaction with outside world
- Faculty competence co-relation with program- specific criteria
- Faculty as participants / resource persons in training and development activities

Facilities and technical support

The details of infrastructural facilities including classrooms, seminar halls, conference halls, faculty rooms, laboratories, animal house, museum, medicinal plant garden needs to be provided under this heading. Details about instruments, equipments and their relevance to curriculum and POs should be indicated.

Teaching-learning process

It includes details about modes of teaching such as lecture, tutorial, seminar, group discussions and details about practical skills in laboratories. In addition, information about students' admission, tutorial / remedial classes / mentoring, teaching and evaluation process, feedback system, self learning, career guidance, training and placement, entrepreneurship cell, co-curricular and extracurricular activities be provided.

Governance, institutional support and financial resources

The program must possess financial resources to fulfill its mission and POs. Details about budgetary planning and its execution should be indicated. Structure of the organization, governance and transparency, public accounting for institution as well as program be indicated.

Continuous improvement

There should be documented process for the periodic review, the PEOs, the POs and the COs. The continuous improvement in the PEOs and POs need to be validated with proper documentation. Improvement in all the important parameters mentioned in eight criteria indicated earlier have to be provided under this heading.

AWARDING ACCREDATION.

Under tier II system, a program scoring minimum 750 points out of 1000 with a minimum score of 60% in mandatory fields (criteria 1, 4, 5, 6, 7, 8) shall be eligible for accreditation of 5 years. A program with a score of 600 points and 60% in mandatory fields (criteria 1, 4, 5, 6, 7, 8) shall be eligible for accreditation for two years.

Steps involved in accreditation process.

Following 6 steps are involved

Step 1: Online registration process (for institution not registered with NBA)

Step 2: Applying for accreditation

Step 3: On site visit of evaluation team to the institute

Step 4: Consideration of evaluation report by Evaluation Accreditation Committee (EAC)

Step 5: Issuance of accreditation status

Step 6: appeal (if any) against the accreditation status

Provisional accreditation to new programs for a year of two years may be offered.

Before accreditation visit, the evaluation committee gives a list of documents which the accredit ting institute should keep ready. During the visit of accreditation, the evaluation committee examines all the documents to ensure that the program deserves the accreditation. In order to have transparency and objectivity, in the evaluation process, the chairperson, evaluators, head of the institution may give one's feedback about others to the NBA using specified forms.

There is a redressal process for award of accreditation. After decision of the award, the institution can make an appeal within thirteen days along-with supporting evidence. The GC / Subcommittee of GC / NBA will consider the findings of the appellate committee and arrive at a final decision within 60 days after the appeal. If appellate committee directs for revisit, the NBA will appoint a reevaluation team after consent from the institution and a second visit may be conducted after receipt of the requisite payment from the institution. If the institution does not agree for revisit, the appeal shall be considered as deemed to be dismissed.

Members of the evaluation team are provided with a document, "Guidelines and operating practices for accreditation visit and evaluation".

After discussion of background and the New Norms of Accreditation in the present section, the readers might have got overview of the revised NBA document. Guidelines and operating practices for accreditation visit and evaluation as well as Self Assessment Report (SAR) for Pharmacy programs are discussed in the subsequent sections.

Chapter 2

EVALUATION CRITERIA

Accreditation is the process of assuring quality of the educational process followed by the institution. For students and their parents, it provides a benchmark describing minimum basic framework and a promise for the educational process. An institution desirous of applying for accreditation is expected to prepare a Self Assessment Report (SAR) divided into two parts. Part A asks for general details about the institution and the program. Part B asks for extensive details about various criteria, based on which accreditation status of the institution will be decided. Part A is further subdivided into fourteen sections dealing with information about the institution and eight sections dealing with program- specific information. Part B deals with nine major criteria pinpointing detailed educational procedures followed by the institution during conduct of the program. Part A of the SAR prepared with the revised version of accreditation document is similar to that of earlier version; whereas in part B there is a major change in approach and detailing. Comparison between old and new criteria of part B is presented in this article.

LINK OF OLD AND NEW CRITERIA:

In the process of accreditation, an institution is evaluated for 1000 marks. In the earlier version of accreditation document, there were eight criteria; while in the recent version, there are nine criteria. The total marks continue to be 1000 in both the cases. The comparison between new and old criteria is presented in Table 1.

Scrutiny of Table 1 makes following points very clear.

Three parameters are quiet new in the fresh norms; Program Educational Objectives (PEOs), Program Outcomes (POs) and Course Outcomes (COs), of which PEOs and POs with Programme Curriculum are components of teaching learning process.Every educational program should be designed with educational objectives in mind. Such objectives should be relevant, unequivocal, observable, measurable and feasible in nature. An educational program, especially of professional nature needs that it should be relevant to existing needs of the society. Further the objectives should be clear and feasible in the environment of the institution. From time to time the attainment of objectives should be observable and measurable so that evaluation in an objective manner can be conducted even by a third party. These objectives are to be assessed in terms of Program outcomes to find out whether identified objectives have been achieved or not; hence program outcome follows PEOs. If PEOs are not achieved as observed in POs, then the gaps are filled up by providing remedial or supplementary continuing education. Every program consists of a set of courses; thus POs, can be followed up by Course Outcomes i.e. COs. As discussed above, PEOs, POs, and COs are interrelated and interdependent.

FUNCTIONING OF EVALUATION COMMITTEES:

The evaluation committee constitutes one chairperson and two evaluators for each programme. The evaluators are expected to perform following functions.

- Study the SAR provided by the institution and identify areas where additional information may be required. Evaluate the SAR, collect and analyze the information.
- Assist the chairperson in conducting the visit
- Ensure that the report is prepared and submitted to the NBA at the end of the final day visit.
- Dos and don'ts by the chairperson and the evaluators have been indicated in the evaluation document.

The evaluation team will visit the institution and validate the assessment of the institution through the SAR as per the specified accreditation criteria. Following points are looked upon by the visiting team.

Outcome of the education provided

- Quality assurance processes including internal reviews
- Assessment
- Activities and work of the students
- Entry standards and selection for admission of students
- Motivation and enthusiasm of the faculty
- Qualification and activities of the faculty members
- Infrastructure facilities
- Laboratory facilities
- Library facilities
- Industry participation and
- Organization

The team will have discussion with head of the institution, heads of the departments, management representatives, faculty members, alumni, students and parents. The team will have visits to classrooms, laboratories pertaining to the program, library, computer centre, hostel and related facilities. The team will check all the documents indicated by NBA and any other document which may be complimentary to the enlisted activities.

The entire process of accreditation visit comprises four activities as indicated below.

- Pre visit activities
- Activities during the visit

- Report writing
- Seeking 360° feedback

360° feedback is a new addition in the NBA process. It involves feedback of stakeholders like institution, chairperson, evaluators and service provider about each other, based on a standard format. It is expected to improve the accreditation system and enhance its effectiveness. It will help in bringing transparency and objectivity in the evaluation process which, in turn improves the quality of accreditation process. As a part of 360° feedback, four forms have been designed.

- Form A : Feedback form to be filled by the institution regarding accreditation visit.
- Form B : Feedback form to be filled by the chairperson about the institution and team members.
- Form C : Feedback form to be filled by the evaluator about the institution, co-evaluator and chairperson.
- Form D : Feedback form to be filled by the Chairperson/Evaluator(s) about service provider.

Formats for all these four forms are available online and they are to be submitted/mailed within three days of the visit.

In future all fresh applicants will be following new criteria only. Hence some highlights of new criteria are discussed in subsequent paragraphs.

VISION AND MISSION:

Institute or department is supposed to list and articulate the vision and mission statement and is to be reflected in media like websites, books etc. The dissemination of these statements among stakeholders needs to be insured, e.g. a pocket card containing academic calendar on a side and vision and mission statements on the other side can be distributed to all teachers and students. When an institute is divided in large sized departments, the vision and mission statements of the departments need to be in line with those of institute e.g. Pharmaceutical care of patients can be vision of a program; while how students are to be trained in order to make them expert in providing pharmaceutical care can be mission of program.

Vision of the institute should be linked to existing professional responsibilities for the students. The responsibilities should be thoroughly discussed by involving all stakeholders i.e. Management, teaching staff, parents, alumni, existing students, supporting staff etc. Records of the meetings with all of them should be appropriately maintained and suggestions from all of them should be incorporated in the document. This makes the event really participatory and takes opinion from all   sectors to make your exercise really meaningful. Once consensus is obtained on the vision, a draft mission statement should be circulated to all the stakeholders to involve them in the process as to how the vision will be translated into actual practice. Mission should indicate how vision is going to be achieved.

PROGRAMME EDUCATIONAL OBJECTIVES (PEOS):

PEOs are broad statements that describe the career and professional accomplishments of the program. PEOs need to be in line with needs of the stakeholders and should also be consistent with mission of the institution. Following stakeholders are related to pharmacy curriculum.

- Students
- Faculty
- Parents
- Management
- Regulatory bodies
- Professional associations
- Drug manufacturers and supply chain
- Patients

All stakeholders collectively expect that students being trained by pharmacy institutions should be able to serve the society for its time dependant changing needs.

Program Educational Objectives (PEOs) constitute the real thrust of the program. In fact PEOs indicate further translation of mission into reality in the form of educational content. One more factor which has to be considered here is professional commitments. What is identified in the vision and mission has to be consistent with actual needs on the field. This should be reflected in the professional requirements. Industry cannot work in isolation of needs of the society. Academic institutions may continue to work in isolation, especially because of regulatory cushion. Recognition from the Council or affiliation with the University is a kind of cushion for academic institutions; however unless actual needs of the society are reflected in the structure and pedagogy of the curriculum, mere curriculum or award of degree/diploma is not enough to guarantee a job. Hence identifying **"RIGHT"** Program Educational Objectives is one important way to rationalize the intent of education. It has to be further continued in program objectives, program outcomes, course objectives and course outcomes; however before caring for POs, and COs, achievement of PEOs need to be assessed.

ACHIEVEMENT OF PEOs:

It is necessary to indicate how subjects in the curriculum help in achieving PEOs; thus subject content should be appropriately designed in line with PEOs. Very often, either PEOs are not well defined before designing the curriculum or else having PEOs identified curricular content do not align themselves to the PEOs. Occasionally there may be problems at the level of implementation. All these gaps need to be bridged in order to have an effective educational process. The important issue is to develop a system of collecting right information which will help us in assessing whether the institute is moving in right direction towards PEOs or otherwise. The instruments needed for assessment should be objective and continuous. Further, collection of the information has to be unbiased. To achieve this, careful planning and implementation, maybe by involving an unbiased outsider knowing intricacies of the educational process is desirable. Various committees should be formulated to identify all aspects related to implementation of the curriculum and co/extracurricular activities and functions of these committees should be described precisely.

ASSESSMENT OF ACHIEVEMENT OF PEOs:

It is not enough merely depicting PEOs, it is necessary to ensure that a periodic assessment should be done whether PEOs are really being achieved or not. Periodicity of the assessment may be decided at the institutional level. Whos and Hows of the assessment are needed to be clarified. Proofs of achievement of PEOs are needed to be described with respect to, expected level of achievement, summaries, documentation and maintenance of the results. Based on the unbiased information obtained in the assessment indicated in earlier section, a factual decision has to be taken to find out whether the institute is really aligned to the PEOs in the letter and spirit or is deviating from the intentions while performing actual implementation. If there is any gap between a cup and a lip, then either the process of education has to be altered or the PEOs have to be redefined in the light of actual happenings.

REDEFINING OF PEOs:

PEOs are not static statements. They need to be redefined based on the feedback of stakeholders and processes for their implementation. Very often it happens that, identified PEOs are not achieved and the practical situation compels us that PEOs need to be modified in view of the real field situation. In such cases realistic feedback from stakeholders is of extreme importance. In addition, the system of identifying PEOs has to be very flexible and should be open to change on the basis of rational feedback. The process of feedback has to be objective in nature.

DEFINITION AND VALIDATION OF COs AND POs:

The COs and POs should first be listed. The media through which POs are published and disseminated to stakeholders should be clearly stated. The description of the process indicating how POs are periodically aligned to graduate attributes and their details with reference to the accreditation manual need to be described. It is also necessary to show correlation between PEOs and POs. Fortunately, NBA has identified the graduate attributes which are broad enough to define Program Outcomes (POs)

ATTAINMENT OF POs:

What is stated in program outcomes needs to be assessed. There is a possibility that in actual practice, what we attain may be different than what we had projected earlier. To examine this, dealing with some sample students, who represent the general population should be is desirable.

There has to be a correlation between POs and COs. The basis of correlation has to be documented. Description of various course delivery methods and their suitability to attainment of POs should be indicated. The type of delivery mode should be justified further by using suitable survey at the end of the course. Description of types of evaluation methods and their relevance to attainment of POs should be indicated. It is necessary to justify balance between theory and practical towards attainment of PEOs and POs. It has to be justified that every component of theory and practicals constituting COs is oriented towards attaining POs.

EVALUATION OF ATTAINMENT OF POs:

Attainment of POs as indicated in point 2.2 has to be further evaluated. Description of the evaluation process documenting and demonstrating the degree to which POs have been attained should be provided. Information on listing and description of the evaluation process and their frequency should be indicated. The instrument which has been used for data collection should be clearly stated. e.g. exam. questions, projects, oral exams etc. Information on the expected level of attainment for each PO, summaries of the results of the evaluation processes and an analysis illustrating the extent to which each PO is attained; and how the results are documented and maintained be provided

REDEFINING POs BASED ON THE FEEDBACK:

During the process of feedback it might be realized that, attainment of POs is not in line with graduate attributes. In such cases POs may have to be redefined/reviewed. Rationale for such observations should be indicated.

CURRICULUM:

Structure of the curriculum should be indicated. Prerequisites for the courses, if any, be schematically presented. It is necessary to provide evidence that the content of the curriculum satisfies applicable program criteria. e.g. Anatomy, Physiology and Health Education (APHE) is a prerequisite for Pharmacology.

CURRICULUM COMPONENTS AND RELEVANCE TO THE POs AND THE PEOs:

Usually pharmacy curriculum can be grouped under four major headings: Pharmaceutics, Pharmaceutical Chemistry, Pharmacology and Pharmacognosy. Fifth group of all other courses not coming under these titles can be placed. Entire curricular content can be conveniently placed under these groups and their relevance to PCs and PEOs should be clearly stated.

CORE COURSES AND THEIR RELEVANCE TO POs:

All courses included under five subheadings indicated in above point are core courses. It should be clarified as to how contents from the core courses develop ability of students to solve professional problems. The sequence of linkage is PEOs – POs – COs. One has to ensure that content of curriculum in terms of core courses is really able to achieve the basic program objective.

INDUSTRY INTERACTION/INTERNSHIP:

Interaction between Pharmaceutical industries and academic institutions is vital for success of the curriculum. Industries have to show involvement in the program in the form of Laboratory related work. It is expected that some part of internship where students can work in Pharmaceutical Industries can be included in the curriculum.

MEASURES AND PROCESSES USED TO IDENTIFY GAPS IN ATTAINMENT OF COS AND POS:

It is possible that the identified COs and POs may not be achieved during implementation of the curriculum. The process to identify gaps if any between identified COs and POs and their actual attainment should be clarified.

CONTENT BEYOND SYLLABUS:

Actual professional needs on the field may change from time to time. In such cases, curricular content indicated in the syllabus may not be enough for attainment of COs and POs. Efforts to offer such necessary contents beyond the syllabi should be stated clearly. Time dependant changes in regulatory requirements should be reflected in the curriculum.e.g. from January 2013, Quality by Design (QbD) has been made mandatory by USFDA for all generic drugs. This part of regulation should now become a part of Pharmacy curriculum.

STUDENTS' PERFORMANCE IN THE PROGRAMME:

Students are to be evaluated based on their success rate, academic performance, placement and higher studies and participation in professional activities. Students are to be encouraged for participation in various conferences, symposia, workshops and presentation of research and review articles therein. Students are also to be encouraged to be members of professional organizations like Indian Pharmaceutical Association (IPA), Indian Society for Technical Education (ISTE) etc.

FACULTY CONTRIBUTION:

Normally faculty contribution is assessed based on student-teacher ratio, faculty-cadre ratio and faculty qualifications. Overall competencies of faculty should be related to program- specific criteria. In addition, participation of faculty as a resource person, research publications of faculty, intellectual property developed by faculty, Research and

Development (R&D) Projects, consultancy and integration of faculty with outside world are added parameters on which the faculty is evaluated. Professional satisfaction of the faculty improves retention in the institute. Thus faculty retention is also a parameter to assess faculty contribution.

FACILITIES AND TECHNICAL SUPPORT:

Availability of infrastructural facilities like adequate class/tutorial rooms, faculty rooms, laboratories, instruments, animal house and related facilities, museum, medicinal plant garden and administrative and technical manpower support and their skill up-gradation are the points on which facilities and technical support can be evaluated.

TEACHING-LEARNING PROCESSES (TLP):

TLP is assessed based on tutorial classes, mentoring system to help students, feedback analysis and corrective measures, scope of self learning, generation of self learning facilities, language laboratories, career guidance, training-placement and entrepreneurship cell, co-curricular and extra-curricular activities, availability of sports facility. TLP should be so effective that for every course, course outcomes should match the course objectives; and if it is not happening, then appropriate instruments including feedback from students should be objectively obtained by an unbiased agency.

GOVERNANCE, INSTITUTIONAL SUPPORT AND FINANCIAL RESOURCES:

It is assessed based on infrastructural facilities in the campus, organization governance and transparency, budget allocation, utilization and accounting (both at institutional and program- specific levels), library, internet, safety norms and checks and emergency medical care and first-aid.

CONTINUOUS IMPROVEMENT:

All the parameters on the basis of which accreditation is accorded to an institute, need to have continuous improvement. Hence parameters like success index of students, performance index of students, improvement in student-teacher ratio enhancement of faculty qualification index and improvement in faculty research publications, R&D and consultancy for last three years need to be evaluated. Appropriate documentation for al parameters should be adequately maintained. Participation in continuing education. generated new facilities and overall improvement since last accreditation need to be evaluated.

As the visit of expert team progresses their work, they prepare a document indicating marks achieved under each subheading as indicated below. Such marks are allotted for each criterion individually. At the end a summary is prepared for all the criteria and an evaluation sheet is prepared in tabular format. The table indicates every criteria, points awarded for each criteria and whether the institution qualifies in individual criteria. All evaluators are expected to sign this mark-sheet. In addition, the chairman prepares the report along-with comments on strengths, weaknesses, deficiencies (if any) and additional remarks (if any). A list of documents is to be prepared in support of SAR. The documents are of two types, institute- specific and program specific. Seventeen institute specific and thirty two program- specific documents have been indicated in the list. List of documents are induced in appendix. It is expected that data regarding above mentioned points for last three years have to be presented.

- NBA has provided a list of illustrative questions under four titles.
- Head of the institution
- Head of the department
- Faculty
- Students

It is advisable that draft answers for all these questions be kept ready by the institution being accreditated.

Table No. 1: Comparison between new and old accreditation criteria.

New			Old	
Criterion No.	**Description**	**Points**	**Criterion No.**	**Description**
1.	Vision, Mission and Program Educational Objectives	75	I	Organization and Governance (Partly)
2.	Program Outcomes	200	VII	Supplementary processes (Partly)
3.	Program Curriculum	100		
7.	Teaching-Learning Process	75	VI	Teaching – Learning Process
			V	Human Resources: Students
4.	Students' Performance in the Program	75	VIII	Research & Development and interaction effort (Partly)
5.	Faculty Contributions	175	IV	Human Resources: Faculty and Staff

			VIII	Research & Development and interaction effort (Partly)
6.	Facilities and Technical Support	150	III	Physical Resources (Central Facilities)
8.	Governance, Institutional Support and Financial Resources	75	I	Organization and Governance (Partly)
			II	Financial Resources, Allocation and Utilization
9.	Continuous Improvement	75		
	Total Points: 1000			Total Marks: 1000

Chapter 3...

DESIGN OF CURRICULUM

Accreditation is a pre-requisite for autonomy for the institution. During autonomy, the institution is supposed to design and implement its own courses. Thus, the purpose of accreditation of professional courses is to find out if institutions seeking accreditation work out, design and implement their educational programs in a professional manner or not. By "professional manner", we mean planning and implementation of "Key" parameters like Mission, Vision, PEOs, POs, and COs in a logical sequence. It is expected that performance in key parameters should be in a dynamic manner, relevant to changing needs of the society around them. If "key "parameters are to be constantly modified, then the reflection of attitude is to be presented in the "Curriculum". Thus, a dynamic curriculum relevant to the changing needs of the society is one of the central factors in Accreditation. Hence much emphasis has been placed on design of the curriculum in the present article. Unfortunately in the conventional model of a large number of affiliated colleges linked to a public-financed University, design of curriculum for a large number of colleges may not be done so seriously so that the changing needs of the society are reflected in the curriculum.

PEOs: While writing Program Education Objectives (PEOs), it should be ensured that content of the PEOs reflect actual field needs of the profession. After identifying professional needs, tasks underlying every objective need to be specified. For performing identified task, a set of Attitude, Knowledge and Skills (A-S-K) should be defined either individually or collectively. Based on these activities, a curriculum should be designed. A designed curriculum is implemented further by the system of education. It involves pedagogy of education. It is expected that all events included in identification of PEOs and implementation of curriculum is one aspect of system.

On the other hand, Program Outcomes (POs), and Course Outcomes (COs) constitute another aspect of the system. They are based on content of the curriculum, and its actual implementation which is based on the field situation. It is interesting to find out whether POs and COs are really capable of achieving PEOs or do they need any corrections. If it is observed that POs and COs are missing in attaining certain PEOs, then appropriate changes should be made in the curriculum so that PEOs on one hand and POs as well as COs on the other hand are perfectly consistent. It is assumed that, COs being part of POs, are consistent with each other. If they are not consistent, then minor changes in COs to get them aligned with identified POs will serve the purpose. The development of POs and COs in consonance with PEOs is the 'process of development of a curriculum'.

Needs of the society are not static. Based on changing needs of the population and constant technological development, every profession evolves with time. The best example is of computers which has transformed probably every profession in leaps and bounds. The changing needs of society should be reflected in modified PEOs. Based on the modified PEOs, POs and COs should be modified in a consistent manner. Fortunately for a profession like pharmacy, changing societal needs is reflected in modified regulations both at national and global level. Based on the regulatory changes, PEOs, POs and COs can be modified.

There are three constant drives, which change the spectrum related to drugs,

1. New diseases are emerging e.g. AIDS, Swine flu etc.

2. New drugs for existing diseases are being developed e.g. new H2 blocker, new dopamine receptor blockers etc.

3. More and more drugs are coming out of patent life and are getting converted to generic drugs.

Since cost of research related to point no. 1 and 2 are on higher side, most of Indian pharmaceutical companies are working in the area of development of generic drugs. WHO concept of essential drugs states that, a limited number of drugs are adequate for controlling diseases of majority population. Such limited number of drugs has been labeled as "Essential Drugs". Since majority of Indian pharmaceutical companies are operating on generic drugs, and majority of Indian population needs affordable drugs, the concept of essential drugs is very vital for India. Thus if entire pharmacy curriculum is designed in such a way that essential drugs form centrality of the curriculum, then the curriculum will turn out to be very relevant to the Indian conditions.

Thus PEOs, POs and COs should revolve around essential drug list as identified by our health professionals. It has to be ensured that PEOs, POs & COs are sequentially linked to each other. If there is any discord between these three components, then appropriate changes in the content of any one of them are desirable. Usually PEOs being gross objectives, they are unlikely to change unless there is any major shift in the emphasis of the profession. It is rare to happen, however it is possible. A minor change in PEOs may be reflected in change in POs. Along-with change in POs, modifications in content of COs is possible. Not only that, new courses may have to be added in order to reflect technological modifications in the content of profession as well as curriculum e.g. courses on nanotechnology, bioinformatics,, human genome, personalized medicine were not necessary few decades back; however these courses can be linked to new job creations. Such courses along-with relevant objectives need to be added with changing technological needs.

Illustrative PEOs for a B. Pharm. Course can be as follows:
- To know physical, chemical and biological properties of drugs.
- To know formulation-related factors of dosage forms.
- To know formulation and evaluation processes.
- To know clinical uses of drugs.
- To know Pathophysiology, Microbiology and Biochemistry related to disease state.
- To know Indian and Global regulations about manufacture and use of drugs.
- To know Quality control and Quality assurance of drugs.
- To know wholesale and retail distribution of drugs.
- To know about stability and storage of drugs.
- To know manufacturing and clinical uses of drugs derived from biotechnology origin.

Illustrative POs for a B. Pharm. Course can be as follows:
At the end of getting B. Pham degree every student should be able to:
- Manufacture any pharmaceutical formulation of drugs by following Good Manufacturing Practices (GMP)
- Evaluate any pharmaceutical formulation following Good Laboratory practices (GLP)
- Store drugs in a stable form.
- Follow practice of all necessary regulations related to manufacture and use of drugs.
- Record action and clinical uses of drugs.
- Record all possible adverse reactions to clinical uses of drugs
- Know and remedy physicochemical interactions amongst drugs and their consequences.
- Record all clinical interactions amongst drugs or with food.
- Participate in clinical trials for clinical records and monitoring of trials.
- Participate in wholesale and retail distribution of drugs in effective manner.

In order to attain PEOs and POs, courses need to be designed and for every course, course objectives (COs) need to be identified. Illustrative list of courses and representative COs for one course are listed herewith.

LIST OF COURSES
- Physical Pharmacy
- Pharmaceutics
- Pharmaceutical Analysis

- Pharmacology
- Pharamcovigilance
- Impurity Profile of drugs
- Biopharmaceutics
- Pharmaceutical Jurisprudence(Indian)
- WHO Good Manufacturing Practices
- Good Laboratory Practices
- Global regulations for drugs
- Clinical Trials
- Clinical Biochemistry
- Clinical Microbiology
- Essential Drugs
- Social Pharmacy
- Indigenous Drugs (Complimentary & Allied Systems)
- Properties of Drugs
- Distribution of Drugs
- Stability of Drugs
- Quality Control & Quality Assurance of Drugs
- Human Anatomy & Physiology
- Clinical Immunology

For every enlisted course, objectives need to be defined. Objectives for one of the course i.e. WHO GMP are given below as an illustration.

Representative Course Objectives for a course on GMP:

- Introduction to WHO GMP
- To understand Quality Management
- To understand sanitation and Hygiene
- To understand Validation
- To handle Complaints and recalls
- To know Contract production and Analysis of Drugs
- To understand self Inspection
- To understand Personnel
- To understand Premises
- To know equipments used for Manufacture of drugs
- To understand Materials used for Manufacture of drugs.
- To Comprehend Documentation related to Manufacture of drugs.

- To Know Manufacture of Sterile Drugs
- To Comprehend about Active Pharmaceutical Ingredients (APIs)

Similar course objectives for every course need to be identified & validated based on opinion of the experts and then consolidated for the purpose of implementation.

Once the course objectives are identified and consolidated by extensive comments from various experts, then detailing of the course content, preparation of learning material, availability of right literature for support, development of evaluation criteria for assessment, development of Question bank, Power-Point presentations can be prepared by the concerned teaching staff in association with experts from Pharmaceutical industries.

Writing PEOs, POs, and COs is only one part of the curriculum. There is much gap between a cup and a lip. All what is identified as a curriculum may find practical issues when it starts getting implemented. Things which have been identified may change with time; the change may be reflected in regulations; it may be reflected in documentation; new supporting literature may be available; trainer's comprehension about the topic may be different.

Usually a professional curriculum consists of three major components; 'what students must know', 'what is useful to know' and 'what is desirable to know'. If contents of these three components are carefully defined, then, the curriculum becomes more precise and effective. Involvement of professionals working on the field during design of the curriculum is very important; because, they are very clear about "basic minimum activities need to be performed by students in order to become effective professionals". This constitutes base of the pyramid of the curriculum. Second and third stage of the pyramid is to add useful to know and desirable to know based on actual needs of the field. Academicians involved in the process of curriculum making should appreciate these facts thoroughly and should consult professionals on the field from time to time so that curriculum satisfies changing needs of society

"Must know" are the areas which every student must understand. These are basic contents of the profession. The second is useful to know. Depending on interest and actual filed needs, a fraction of students may know these areas fully or partially. Third is desirable to know areas. It indicates the optional areas where a section of students with special needs may desire to know. These may be newer additions in the profession.

Following topics are illustrative only. Few additional topics may be added or deleted depending on the actual training needs

MUST KNOW AREAS

Basic sciences relevant to physical, chemical and biological properties of drugs constitute must know areas. Clinical uses of drugs, Pharmacovigilance, Stability and storage of drugs, Functional Human anatomy & Physiology, Biochemistry and Microbiology as related to mechanism of action of drugs. WHO concept of essential drugs. Indian laws related to manufacture, distribution and uses of drugs with emphasis on cGMP, Vaccines, Sera; Patents about drugs and dosage forms.

USEFUL TO KNOW AREAS

Marketing of drugs, Global regulations of drugs, Synthesis of drugs, Analysis of drugs, Botany of medicinal plants, Standardization of Indigenous drugs can be useful to know ares,

DESIRABLE TO KNOW AREAS

Social Pharmacy, Biosimilars, Monoclonal antibodies, Global drug market, International Conference on Harmonization (ICH),Professional associations related to Pharmacy, Complimentary and Allied Systems of Medicine (CAM) as identified by WHO, Global regulations about CAM, Export documentation related to drugs can be desirable to know areas.

Shifting of a topic from one area to another may be done with changing emphasis related to the profession on the field.

The courses listed under 'must know area' are the core courses. They should contain 65 to 70 % of the curriculum. Useful to know and Desirable to know together are expected to contain about 30% of the curriculum.

Live interaction with industry is one way of keeping the courses updated. Industry cannot survive unless new products and new technologies are incorporated in its day-to-day functioning. Such rapid changes are necessary for surviving in the h ghly competitive world. In addition, global regulatory changes followed by reflection in local regulatory requirements are one of the prime drivers of industrial change. If academic institutions keep updated along-with changes in the industrial scenario, it has to be reflected in the curricular changes. It has been pointed out that 5-10% curricular change every year is an eventual possibility. In order to meet such changes, existing faculty of academic institutions have to keep pace with rapid industrial changes and modify the curriculum accordingly.

Gaps in the knowledge with respect to changing regulatory and industrial changes need to be identified and offered in the form of short term continuing education courses. Content beyond syllabus is a common requirement for all time to come. Annual proceedings of professional bodies like Indian Pharmaceutical Association (IPA), Indian Pharmacological Society (IPS), Indian Drug Manufacturers' Association (IDMA), Organization of Pharmaceutical Producers of India (OPPI), Indian Chemical Manufacturers' Association (ICMA), Pharmaceutical and Allied Manufacturers' and Distributors' Association Limited (PAMDAL) provides indication of challenges faced by the partners in that year. It is necessary that a periodic review of proceedings of professional bodies should be first given to faculty and then to students at least once in few years.

Experts from various areas who have field experience should participate in training of students so that actual needs of the profession "as they need" are sensitized by the students. Filling up gaps in knowledge is a constant ongoing activity to match POs and COs with PEOs on continual basis.

Chapter 4...

CHANGE OF MINDSET

Whenever any institution desires for accreditation, one has to be very clear as to why the institution is venturing in the exercise. Since 95% of the institutions in India are in the private sector, the first party who should get convinced about accreditation is the management running the institution. The biggest advantage for an acceditated institution is that of international equalization of their graduate with the graduate of other countries who have signed Washington Accord. Till date, 17 countries have signed the accord including old timers like Australia, Canada, New Zealand, United Kingdom and United States of America from 1989 and few other developed countries like Japan, Korea later. India has joined only in 2014. Once equalization of degree is accorded, acceptability of graduates from India to all other countries who are signatories to Washington accord will be easier. However for this thing to happen, a lot of other related factors have to change; and first factor to be changed is that of mindset.

No education is meaningful unless objectives for offering it are clearly stated. It is of still more importance, if the education is for a professional degree. Professional practice has constantly changing perspectives based on changing needs of the society. In addition, society is very clear on its expectations from the profession. It is left to the profession to understand the needs correctly and translate them in education properly. If translation of real needs of the society is not reflected correctly in the education of students, then either the educational process becomes redundant or the society finds some other alternatives to fulfill its obligations. This has been happening for all professions. Change of mindset is necessary here. Unless the managements providing education realize that the education provided in their institutes really makes students immediately employable; or make them worthy of entrepreneurship based on needs of the society, admissions to their colleges are going to be questionable. Mere recognition by regulatory authorities is not enough to continue in the market place. The real taste of vulnerability of an educational institute is how better their students perform in the real competitive world which is so dynamic and full of uncertainties.

The second big change should be in the mindset of teaching faculty. For any progressive educational institute, the core anchor on which, credibility of the institute rests is the commitment of teaching faculty. Employability or entrepreneurship is one of the twin major objectives for any professional teaching institute. For this to happen, mere curriculum is not enough; because factors related to employment/ entrepreneurship are not being considered seriously while designing the curriculum. Faculty teaches what they know; rather than what is needed on the field. Occasionally the faculty may not be really aware of what is needed on the field. The real connect between aspiring students and the enterprising employers are missing to the disadvantage of students. As a result, what we exert is an implementation of a skeleton of education in the form of curriculum and examination while missing the soul in the form of problem-solving capacity and hence employability/ entrepreneurship in the real life. The only solution to this s implementing objective-based education dependent on actual needs of the society. Fortunately accreditation is providing a wonderful opportunity for such things to happen. Faculty of private unaided institutions has to convincingly realize that mere implementation of University curriculum is not enough for their survival; it needs to be strongly complemented through additional efforts in the form of necessary soft skills, specialized training in niche areas related to employability/entrepreneurship, and a smart outlook towards dynamic needs of society and employers. The delivery of educational content has to be based on individual needs of every student in a personalized manner. Identification of Program Educational Objectives (PEOs), assessment and evaluation of Program Outcomes (POs) and Course Outcomes (COs) are the means towards achieving the fact that program content is really meaningful. The teaching faculty should change their mindset in merely not sticking to the University Curriculum.

An equally important change in mindset has to be in the thinking of students. If they believe that what is being taught in the curriculum is enough to withstand the uncertainties of future, then they are misguided. The award of a degree or diploma is also not a guarantee for their employability/ entrepreneurship. What matters is their proactive behavior towards the needs of real life in the form of demands of employers or the expectations of society in the form of an enterprise. In this context passive dependence on expertise of teaching faculty is not enough. The students should look beyond the horizon of educational institute and acquire necessary knowledge and skills through life-long learning. Continuing education programs of short duration lasting from one day to one week or more through experts working on the field are equally important. The students should be very much after the teaching faculty to ensure that such training offered by employers is of extreme importance in increasing their employment potential. One-to-one linkage with employer and the institute is very much desirable. In addition, a credible resource is of alumni of the institute with whom, existing students should maintain a strong rapport. The existing students should invite alumni working in different professional areas and know their job content. Lesser the age difference between the alumni counselors and existing students, more effective is the advice; hence frequent visits of fresh alumni to the parent institute is a vital bargain by existing students. Changing requirements of employers with progressing time can be well known by interaction with alumni.

The change of mindset of the management, faculty and the students has also to trickle down to one more major stakeholder i.e. supporting staff. The supporting staff is present in the teaching institute itself. Many times they are taken for granted. Training of supporting staff is a neglected area. It is felt both by the management and teaching staff that a cursory inclusion of supporting staff in the process of accreditation is enough to orient them to the entire process; however it is not realized that a willing involvement knowing the importance and philosophy of the accreditation will orient supporting staff in more effective manner. The supporting staff belongs to following subtypes: Office staff for secretarial assistance, financial detailing and regulatory submissions. The second category is of Library staff involved in procurement of necessary books as per regulatory requirement and providing the educational infrastructure to the best interest of students and faculty. The third category is of manpower for stores to procure and supply machinery, equipments, glassware and chemicals for the entire institute. The fourth category is of laboratory assistants and technicians to maintain all instruments in the laboratories along with chemicals and glassware. One more category of diminishing importance is of animal house keeper. Above all another important category is of manual labors in the form of peons who are spread over all laboratories, library, stores and office. Although job content of peons is only to follow up manual work, their willing involvement in the process of accreditation realizing importance of why they are doing all accreditation-related work will go a long way in improving quality of their input. Training of all these supporting staff to the actual requirements of their job content to be handled in an effective manner is necessary. Hence their training should not be taken casually.

Two more stakeholders need special mention; One is "Parents" and the next is "Employers" Parents have a feeling that once they pay fees to the institute regularly, their job is over. The next feeling is that necessary care of their wards will be fully taken by the Institute and they need not bother much about day-to-day activities of their wards. The feeling is only partially true. The parents do need to follow up frequently about compatibility of their wards to the new environment, both physically and mentally. It is possible that as the ward gets adjusted to the new environment, then the frequency of visits or enquiry may go down; but maintaining a constant rapport with both the ward and teaching faculty of the institute is beneficial for parents in ensuring better adjustment of their ward to the teaching institute. Availability of good cultural and sports facilities on the campus is extremely beneficial for students to get adjusted to the environment easily. This is of special importance if the campus is residential in nature.

Employers have a feeling that due to constantly changing job content of their employees, brand of the institute along with track record of alumni is enough for better campus selection. This is only partially true. A constant vigil on the suitability of their campus recruitments is necessary to avoid complacence on the part of teaching institutes. Further, a constant link with the parent institute in terms of changing job-profiles, changing skill - needs and other generic skills by Human Resources Department of the company is extremely useful for the employer. Such actions may reduce training needs of the industries and may help in having more efficient success rate of selection. A short training module by the industry to the students before graduation can help in reducing man-hunt of the industry on one hand and improve employability of the institute on the other hand. Cost of such training can be shared by the institute and the industry. This can turn out to be an effective way of Industry-Institute- interaction.

Thus, if all stakeholders in the process of training change their existing conventional mindset and make students at the centre of the process of training, then the process of quality assurance of education can be more rewarding in the form of Accreditation. Identification of clear, realistic Program Educational Objectives and its serious implementation by involvement of all stakeholders is extremely necessary for the success of Accreditation. This is more easy to be said than to be done because actual implementation of this philosophy needs constant vigil and a strong willpower in the minds of all stakeholders.

Chapter 5

WHAT SHOULD BE DONE IN INDIA?

The actions to be taken are broadly divided into three categories;

- Actions to be taken by Central/ State Government
- Actions to be taken by Universities/ Colleges
- Actions to be taken at Professional level

Before defining actions to be taken by each category it is necessary to identify all stake holders which need to be consulted. An illustrative list of stake holders is presented below;

- Central Government:
  Ministry of Human Resource Development (AICTE)
  Ministry of Health (PCI) and its state branches
  Ministry of Chemicals & Fertilizers (Department of Pharmaceuticals)
- State Government
  Ministry of Higher and Technical Education
  Ministry of Health (Food and Drug Administration)
- Manufacturers
  Indian Drug Manufacturers Association (IDMA)
  Organization of Pharmaceutical Producers of India (OPPI)
  Indian Pharmaceutical Alliance (IPA)
- Distributors
  All India Chemist and Druggist Association (AICOD) and its state branches
- Professional Associations
  Indian Pharmaceutical Association (IPA)
  Association of Pharmaceutical Teachers of India (APTI)
- Consumer Associations
  Voluntary Health Association of India (VHAI) and its allied NGOs.

Actions to be taken by Central/ State Government

The first initiative which Government of India should initiate is to call all stakeholders to identify vision for the profession of Pharmacy in India for coming decade. Once the vision for the profession is identified it has to be ratified by all stakeholders by the process of consensus. During the process of consultation stakeholders may suggest certain modifications based on their inputs. Once the consensus document is prepared the vision has to be translated into one or more missions. Further the mission is to be subdivided into several objectives. The identification of the objectives will help the profession to define the competencies needed by the professionals. Once the competencies are identified then the necessary attitude, knowledge and the skill needed for achieving these competencies should be clarified. The competencies, relevant objectives and necessary knowledge, skill and attitude will be helpful to design the curriculum.

Actions to be taken by Universities/ Colleges

The knowledge component of the curriculum should be incremental in nature. This indicates that most primitive part should be dealt with initially as a pre requisite for the entire topic. The next related development should follow the basic pre requisite. Linkage of the two components should be emphasized while explaining the developed part. Each sub component of the curriculum should be handled with the analogy of a ladder. Each lower step should lead to the next step and so on. The next important point s of integration. When different sub components of the curriculum are dealt with, their interrelation should be explained well. Overlap of the topics can be dealt with optimum repetitive components. As a specific case few contents of Pharmacy curriculum are illustrated below;

Before discussing anti asthmatic drugs, relevant physiology of the respiratory system and patho physiology of asthma should be elaborated. In addition medicinal chemistry of anti asthmatic drugs should be integrated along with this topic. Structure-activity-relationship of anti asthmatic drugs should be discussed simultaneously along with discussion of pharmacology of anti-asthmatic drugs. Thus when drugs acting on asthma are being discussed entire issue should be discussed in a integrated manner. In the present curriculum more basic pillars of Pharmacy viz. namely Pharmaceutics. Pharmaceutical Chemistry, Pharmacology and Pharmacognosy are handled in an independent unrelated manner with strict compartments. Integration of Pharmacy as a whole is missing.

Without definition of competencies design of curriculum is of limited meaning. Competencies have to be related to the objectives of the profession and objectives of the profession have to be linked to vision of the profession. If this link between curriculum-competencies-objectives-needs of the consumers is properly maintained then the professional curriculum becomes more meaningful. World over the profession of Pharmacy is identified with Pharmaceutical care of patients. Variable patient is at the centre of therapy and Pharmacists have to adjust the therapy to the optimum benefit of patients. Entire Pharmacy profession is built around patient care. Hence the curriculum of Pharmacy is designed into following sub components;

Actions to be taken at Professional level

Representatives of professional associations should help academicians in identifying necessary competencies which are needed on the field while performing the job responsibilities on the field. A noteworthy point is that the professional needs are changing constantly. Professions have to adapt to these changes immediately. They may not survive without immediate adoption to the changing needs. Such a compulsion may not be there for academicians. If the interaction between professionals and academicians is weak then the ultimate losers are students. Students may get a summative appraisal in the form of a degree, diploma, post graduation or doctoral degree may only be a stamp without necessary competencies in the students. Thus a constant dialogue between professionals and academicians and a consequent sustained modification in the curriculum is necessary for quality of the education to be maintained.

Unlike the curriculum being propagated worldwide Indian Pharmacy curriculum of B.Pharm is still revolving on products only. It is not centered on patients. Biomedical component is limited while synthetic and analytical chemistry is dominating. The biggest objection towards the curriculum is as follows;

- It is not based on objectives
- Patient care has limited importance
- It is less integrated
- Pharmacy practice itself has not grown professionally on the field
- As a result, independent job opportunities in Pharmaceutical care have not been generated at all
- Without practical implementation, definition of competencies is meaningless
- On the national scene, vision of Pharmacy profession itself is not well defined

All these happenings constitute vicious circle. Hence following suggestion is made not only to define objectives of the profession but also to identify the competencies needed by Pharmacists and also to link them with curriculum so that the profession gets a recognizable status similar to Global Pharmacists practicing all over the world. The suggestion should be taken as an illustration by all stakeholders in a constructive manner. Any deficiency in the suggestion should be corrected appropriately and a draft acceptable to all stakeholders should be evolved by consensus.

One may wonder how all this is related to accreditation. Accreditation is a process of quality assurance. Quality assurance expects that parameters in the process of development should be defined properly. Above all quality should be related to needs of consumers. If needs of consumers are not fulfilled, the entire process of quality assurance becomes questionable. As a consequence, utility of the profession itself becomes doubtful. The status of the professional goes down and admission to the course becomes scanty. I believe that Indian pharmacy profession is really struggling for the identity and the worst hit component of this lack of identity is pharmacy education itself.

The proposed objectives of the profession, tasks, and duties of Pharmacists are listed below as an illustration. The documents needs to be debated, commented upon by all stakeholders and actual duties of all stakeholders need to be added to this document. Based on such a revised document the process of design of curriculum should start.

The suggestions are based on a consultation document of World Health Organization (WHO) and few more related documents.

I. OBJECTIVES OF PHARMACY EDUCATION

1.1 Providing manpower for drug regulatory control and management.

1.2 Providing trained community pharmacists.

1.3 Providing trained hospital pharmacists.

1.4 Providing manpower for manufacture, quality control and quality assurance of drugs.

1.5 Providing manpower for marketing of drugs.

1.6 Providing manpower for teaching institutions associated with pharmacy education.

1.7 Providing manpower to professional bodies related to pharmacy and health-related agencies.

1.8 Developing standards for indigenous drugs.

1.9 Rationalizing drugs related to indigenous systems of medicine.

2. TASKS OF PHARMACISTS

2.1 Regulatory control & drug management

2.2 Community Pharmacist

2.3 Hospital Pharmacist

2.4 Industrial Pharmacist

2.5 Academic activities

2.6 Training of other health care workers.

2.7 Working in professional bodies & health related agencies.

The tasks can be further detailed in the form of duties. The detailing is illustrative only.

3. DUTIES OF PHARMACISTS

3.1 Regulatory control & drug management

3.1.1 Health & drug policy.

3.1.2 Management,

3.1.3 Administration.

3.1.4 Educational policy.

3.1.5 Regulatory & enforcement agencies.

3.1.6 Professional registration authority.

3.1.7 International agencies & professional bodies.

3.2 Community pharmacist

3.2.1   Processing of prescriptions.

3.2.2   Care of patients and clinical pharmacy.

- Monitoring of drug utilization.

3.2.3   Extemporaneous preparation & small-scale manufacturing of medicines.

- Traditional & alternative medicines.

3.2.4   Responding to symptoms of minor ailments.

        1.2.4.1   Informing health care professional and the public.

        1.2.4.2   Health promotion.

        1.2.4.3   Domiciliary services.

3.2.5   Agricultural and veterinary practice.

3.3 Hospital Pharmacist

3.3.1   Rational prescribing and use of drug and

3.3.2   Interaction with Wm specialists / expertise.

3.3.3   Recognizing and reporting Adverse Drug Reactions (ADR).

3.3.4   Monitoring patterns of drugs use.

3.3.5   Drug therapeutics committee / formulary.

3.3.6   Educating other health professionals about rational use of drugs.

3.3.7   Therapeutic Drug Monitoring / Analysis.

3.3.8   Manufacturing and Procurement of drugs.

3.3.9   Planning and implementation of clinical trials.

3.4 Industrial Pharmacist

3.4.1   Research and Development (R&D)

3.4.2   Manufacturing, Quality Assurance, Quality Control

3.4.3   Drug information

3.4.4   Patent application and Drug registration.

3.4.5   Clinical trials and Post-Marketing Surveillance (PMS).

3.4.6   Sales and Marketing of drugs.

3.4.7   Management.

3.5 Academic activities

3.5.1   Education

3.5.2   Pharmacy Practice.

3.53   Research

3.6 Training of other health care workers.

3.6.1   Reducing drug abuse in the community

3.6.2   Medical /other suppliers.

3.6.3   Community health workers.

3.6.4   Training of nursing staff

3.6.5   Training of other health workers on the field

3.7   Working in professional bodies & health related agencies.

3.7.1   World Health Organization (WHO).

3.7.2   International Narcotics Control Board.

3.7.3   United Nations Division of Narcotic Drugs.

3.7.4   United Nations Commission on Narcotic Drugs. a United Nations Fund for Drug Abuse Control.

3.7.5   Interpol

3.7.6   National Pharmacopoeial Committees.

3.7.7   Pharmaceutical Societies.

Once the tasks and duties are identified, the crucial job is to identify competencies involved in each one of the duties. An illustrative list of competencies for practicing professional pharmacists is presented here.

4.   PROFESSIONAL COMPETENCIES FOR TASKS &DUTIES OF PHARMACICSTS

- Evaluate drug orders or prescriptions accurately and safety
- Compound drugs in appropriate dosage forms, packages and dispense dosage forms,
- Manage system for storage, preparation and dispensing of medicines.
- Supervise technical personnel involved in the process.
- Manage and administer a pharmacy and pharmacy practice.
- Apply computer skills and technological advancements to practice.
- Communicate with health professionals and patients regarding rational drug therapy; well- being and health promotion.
- Design, implement, monitor, evaluate and modify or recommend modifications in drug therapy to ensure effective, safe and economical patient care.
- Identify, assess and solve medication-treated problems and provide clinical judgement for continuing effectiveness of individualized therapeutic plans and intended therapeutic   outcomes.
- Evaluate patients' and order medications and/or laboratory tests in accordance with established standards of practice.
- Evaluate patients' problems and direct patients to other health professionals for appropriate advice and administer medications.

- Monitor and counsel patients regarding the purposes, uses and effects of their medications and related therapy.
- Understand relevant diet, nutrition and non-drug therapies.
- Recommend, counsel and monitor the patient for use of nonprescription drugs
- Provide first-aid care.
- Retrieve, evaluate and manage professional information and literature.
- Use clinical data to optimize therapeutic drug regimens.
- Collaborate with other health professionals.
- Evaluate and document interventions and pharmaceutical care outcomes.

All the competencies mentioned above are primarily directed to pharmacy practice. The practice of pharmacy will involve tasks needed for community pharmacists and hospital pharmacists. There is a need to identify competencies needed for industrial, regulatory and academic tasks also. A British document in this context is included in the appendix. Having all the competencies put together it should be examined what are the job responsibilities on the field and do they need training of all components and upto what extent. e.g. if hospital and clinical tasks go hand in hand, then a separate degree curriculum for them is desirable. Similarly if Industrial pharmacists do not need clinical or hospital tasks in their day-to-day practice, then they need not be burdened with curriculum oriented towards related tasks. Regulatory and academic tasks also need special mention in view of the tasks involved in them. It is possible that based on proposed job responsibility, "Must know component" may change (See Section 3 (page 3.5)). Along with change in Must know, useful to know and desirable to know areas may also change. A judicious combination of desirable modules can be offered depending on professional needs. The educational system should be flexible enough to accommodate the changing needs of the education. The present rigid structure of more number of affiliated colleges to state-based universities does not offer this kind of flexibility. Hence a major structural change in the educational system involving role of Pharmacy Council of India is needed to incorporate following components.

- Role of Pharmacists in Indian Healthcare system should be defined precisely.
- Based on the defined role, tasks, duties and competencies needed by pharmacists should be identified.
- If the set of competencies is too large, then they may be suitably categorized in two to three units.
- Manpower need for each unit of categories be computed by a competent authority.
- Appropriate flexible curriculum based on manpower needs to be developed by educational institutions.
- Strict objective-based Accreditation criteria for every educational entity should be evolved by the Pharmacy Council of India.

- All these activities should be done only after thorough consultation with all the stakeholders.
- Consensus document should be evolved from the discussion of all stakeholders.
- There should be scope for modification in curricular needs based on demands on the field continuously.
- Present rigidity in the curriculum should be dispensed forthwith.

Identification of competencies needed by Indian pharmacists is an extremely vital area which needs to be concentrated. As a guideline, competencies identified in other developed countries are presented in the Appendix. Unless competencies are identified, what pharmacists are expected to perform is not clear; in absence of such situation national objectives, state objectives, University objectives are vague. Even the council devoted for Pharmacy, i.e. Pharmacy Council of India has not identified specific competencies needed at different professional levels viz. Diploma, Degree. Post graduation or Doctoral education. Pharm. D. is probably the latest addition. Hence there is an urgent need that specific competencies which are relevant to Indian conditions should be identified by consulting all stakeholders. There are conflicts of interest amongst different stakeholders related to pharmacy profession itself. Instead of developing a consensus statement by ironing out conflicts of interests amongst stakeholders, the competencies are left to the choice of working professionals themselves. In absence of competencies identified at national level, states, universities, pharmacy colleges are left to their own individual choice to develop vision or mission statements based on their own discretion. Even if a college identifies a highly unusual vision statement for its own college based on global scenario, the actual ground situation is frustratingly difficult to make pharmaceutical care as the vision of its choice. Global standards are only a cosmetic choice for us.

Are we training our pharmacy graduates only for industries, may be Indian or global? The answer is hesitatingly yes. Are we training our Pharmacy graduates for Pharmaceutical care of Indian patients? The answer is emphatically no. Are Indian holders of Pharm.D. so competent that they can clear all competencies identified in NAPLEX document and competent to get registered in USA? The answer is emphatically no. Are they competent to take pharmaceutical care of Indian patients at least? The negative answer to many of these questions lies in the fact that competencies are not at all identified at any level. If we first identify competencies for every level of pharmacy profession and then generate a curriculum which is consistent with the identified competencies, then professional education in pharmacy will be more meaningful and relevant to Indian conditions. Mere utterance of global criteria without relevance to Indian conditions and competencies may only isolate us to our own peril.

Criteria for accreditation of continuing education should be defined. It is expected that credit system will be implemented in all types of education. In such case, credits should be offered to units of continuing education. Objective criteria for deciding units of continuing education should be identified. It is necessary that content of continuing education should be validated by a team of experts based on objective criteria. Writing articles on continuing education, as identified and validated by experts along with selected precise multiple choice questions can be published in professional journals. A reader is expected to attempt the multiple choice questions and offer answers for MCQs. After evaluation of MCQs a reader getting fixed minimum percentage of marks, say 70% can be given units of continuing education. It can be further announced that minimum accumulation of fixed units of continuing education can be linked to continuation of registration for 1 or 2 academic years. Such an arrangement can open a way for life-long-learning of pharmacists. This can be very relevant to working professionals in India.

Chapter 6...

ACCREDITATION OF PHARMACY INSTITUTIONS IN USA

In USA the process of Accreditation of Pharmacy institutions has been taken very seriously by all stake holders. The process for Accreditation from 2015 was initiated way back in 2003. A document entitled "Future Vision of Pharmacy Practice 2015" was generated by Joint Commission of Pharmacy Practitioners (JCCP) after consulting following seven member pharmacy practitioner groups

- Academy of Managed Care Pharmacy (AMCP)
- American College of Apothecaries (ACP)
- American College of Clinical Pharmacy (ACCP)
- American Pharmacists Association (AphA)
- American Society of Consultant Pharmacists (ASCP)
- American Society of Health-System Pharmacists (ASHP)
- National Community Pharmacists Association (NCPA).

In addition, following four liaison members were also consulted.

- Accreditation Council for Pharmacy Education (ACPE)
- American Association of Colleges of Pharmacy (AACP)
- National Association of Boards of Pharmacy (NABP)
- National Council of State Pharmacy Association Executives (NCSPAE).

All these eleven associations after mutual consultation endorsed a common vision of the preferred future for Pharmacy by 2015. This document entitled "JCCP Future Vision of Pharmacy Practice "is a consensus document which articulates a vision for pharmacy and how it will be practiced. The process started way back in 2004.

The Future Vision of Pharmacy practice generated a vision statement which included; The foundation of Pharmacy Practice, How Pharmacists will Practice; and How Pharmacy Practice Will Benefit Society. Contents of the document are presented below:

FUTURE VISION OF PHARMACY PRACTICE 2015

Vision Statement

Pharmacists will be the health care professionals responsible for providing patient care that ensures optimal medication therapy outcomes.

Pharmacy Practice in 2015

The Foundations of Pharmacy Practice: Pharmacy education will prepare pharmacists to provide patient-centered and population-based care that optimizes medication therapy; to manage health care system resources to improve therapeutic outcomes; and to promote health improvement, wellness, and disease prevention. Pharmacists will develop and maintain:

- a commitment to care for, and care about, patients
- an in-depth knowledge of medications and the biomedical, sociobehavioral, and clinical sciences
- the ability to apply evidence-based therapeutic principles and guidelines, evolving sciences and emerging technologies, and relevant legal, ethical, social, cultural, economic, and professional issues to contemporary pharmacy practice

How Pharmacists Will Practice: Pharmacists will have the authority and autonomy to manage medication therapy and will be accountable for patients' therapeutic outcomes. In doing so, they will communicate and collaborate with patients; care givers, health care professionals, and qualified support personnel. As experts regarding medication use, pharmacists will be responsible for:

- rational use of medications, including the measurement and assurance of medication therapy outcomes
- promotion of wellness, health improvement, and disease prevention
- Design and oversight of safe. accurate, and timely medication distribution systems
- Working cooperatively with practitioners of other disciplines to care for patients, pharmacists will be:
  - o the most trusted and accessible source of medications and related devices and supplies
  - o the primary resource for unbiased information and advice regarding the safe, appropriate, and cost-effective use of medications
  - o valued patient care providers whom health care systems and payers recognize as having responsibility for assuring the desired outcomes of medication use

How Pharmacy Practice Will Benefit Society: Pharmacists will achieve public recognition that they are essential to the provision of effective health care by ensuring that:

- medication therapy management is readily available to all patients
- desired patient outcomes are more frequently achieved
- overuse, underuse, and misuse of medications are minimized
- medication-related public health goals are more effectively achieved
- cost-effectiveness of medication therapy is optimized

FOUNDATIONS FOR PHARMACY CURRICULUM

In addition to these efforts on professional front, additional guidance on Science Foundation needed for the Pharmacy curriculum was also developed. It included elements of Science foundation which was considered essential to the development of pharmacists. The document included four major headings under which entire curriculum of pharmacy should be designed. The headings are as under;

- Basic Biomedical Sciences
- Pharmaceutical Sciences
- Social/Behavioral/Administrative Pharmacy Sciences
- Clinical Sciences

Subject headings under each category has also been further identified

1. Basic Biomedical Sciences

1.1   Anatomy and Physiolgy

1.2   Pathology / Pathophysiology

1.3   Microbiology

1.4   Immunology

1.5   Biochemistry/ Biotechnology

1.6   Molecular Biology/ Genetics

1.7   Biostatistics

2. Pharmaceutical Sciences

2.1   Medicinal Chemistry

2.2   Pharmacology

2.3   Pharmacognosy and Alternative and Complementary Treatments

2.4   Toxicology

2.5   Bioanalysis / Clinical Chemistry

2.6   Pharmaceutics/ Biopharmaceutics

2.7   Pharmacokinetics/ Clinical Pharmacokinetics

2.8   Pharmacogenomics/Genetics

2.9   Extemporaneous Compounding/Parenteral/ Enteral

3. Social/Behavioral/Administrative Pharmacy Sciences

3.1   Healh Care Delivery Systems

3.2   Economics/Pharmacoeconomics

3.3   Practice Management

3.4   Pharmacoepidemiology

3.5   Pharmacy Law and Regulatory Affairs

3.6   History of Pharmacy

3.7   Ethics

3.8   Professional communication

3.9   Social and Behavioral Aspects of Practice

4   Clinical Sciences

4.1   Pharmacy Practice and Pharmacist-Provided Care

4.2   Medication Dispensing and Distribution Systems

4.3   Pharmacotherapy

4.4   Pharmacist-Provided Care for Special Populations

4.5   Drug Information

4.6   Medication Safety

4.7   Literature Evaluation and Research Design

4.8   Patient Assessment Laboratory

ELECTIVE COURSES

A look at the list of courses indicates that every course is identified on the basis of knowledge, attitude and skills required for the conduct of the profession and the vision of the profession as identified by the experts including all stake holders. The consent of all stake holders is taken well in advance so that content of curriculum is all inclusive. It is special to note that Social/Behavioral/Administrative Pharmacy Sciences include one full section of the curriculum indicating that pharmacists need enough training in these sciences in order to become more effective. In addition Clinical sciences also contain one more equally important part of the curriculum. Both these components are notably missing in our Indian curricula. Our curricula are more product-oriented than patient oriented. Content related to Organic Chemistry as related to synthetic aspects of drugs is substantial and the social aspects of the profession are entirely missing. Clinical sciences have a secondary role in our curricula. Emphasis on Pharmacognosy is questionable with respect to quantum of usage of drugs. All these things happen primarily because objectives of the profession are ill-defined and all stake holders are not involved in the process of curriculum design in as transparent manner as it is being done in USA. A wider debate on the issue of Role of Pharmacists in Indian Health care system is desirable by all stake holders before framing the curriculum. Design of curriculum should not be an exercise in isolation by academicians alone with a nominal involvement of Pharmaceutical Experts in a casual manner.

STANDARDS FOR ACCREDITATION

In the American system, Accreditation criteria are identified under six headings. The titles are as follows.

- Standards for Mission, Planning, and Evaluation
- Standards for Organization and Administration
- Standards for Curriculum
- Standards for Students
- Standards for Faculty and Staff
- Standards for Facilities and Resources

All major standards are further subdivided totally in 30 standards and every standard is supported by adequate guidelines. The titles of all major and minor standards are listed below;

STANDARDS FOR MISSION, PLANNING, AND EVALUATION

- Standard No. 1: College or School Mission and Goals
- Standard No. 2: Strategic Plan
- Standard No. 3: Evaluation of Achievement of Mission and Goals

STANDARDS FOR ORGANIZATION AND ADMINISTRATION

- Standard No. 4: Institutional Accreditation
- Standard No. 5: College or School and University Relationship
- Standard No. 6: College or School and other Administrative Relationships
- Standard No. 7: College or School Organization and Governance
- Standard No. 8: Qualifications and Responsibilities of the Dean

STANDARDS FOR CURRICULUM

- Standard No. 9: The Goal of the Curriculum
- Standard No. 10: Curricular Development, Delivery, and Improvement
- Standard No. 11: Teaching and Learning Methods
- Standard No. 12: Professional Competencies and Outcome Expectations
- Standard No. 13: Curricular Core—Knowledge, Skills, Attitudes, and Values
- Standard No. 14: Curricular Core—Pharmacy Practice Experiences
- Standard No. 15: Assessment and Evaluation of Student Learning and Curricular Effectiveness.

STANDARDS FOR STUDENTS

- Standard No. 16: Organization of Student Services
- Standard No. 17: Admission Criteria, Policies, and Procedures
- Standard No. 18: Transfer of Credits and Waiver of Requisites for Admission with Advanced Standing
- Standard No. 19: Progression of Students
- Standard No. 20: Student Complaints Policy
- Standard No. 21: Program Information
- Standard No. 22: Student Representation and Perspectives
- Standard No. 23: Professional Behavior and Harmonious Relationships

STANDARDS FOR FACULTY AND STAFF

- Standard No. 24: Faculty and Staff Quantitative Factors
- Standard No. 25: Faculty and Staff Qualitative Factors
- Standard No. 26: Faculty and Staff Continuing Professional Development and Performance Review

STANDARDS FOR FACILITIES AND RESOURCES

- Standard No. 27: Physical Facilities
- Standard No. 28: Practice Facilities
- Standard No. 29: Library and Educational Resources
- Standard No. 30: Financial Resources

It is very useful to identify as to how every standard is discussed with supporting guidelines. Hence one example of standard for Mission, planning and evaluation is reproduced below. Similar details for other guidelines are available in the ACPE document for the purpose.

STANDARDS FOR MISSION, PLANNING, AND EVALUATION

The purpose of the standards in this section is to ensure that the college or school professional degree program has a clearly articulated mission, desired goals, and that a strategic planning process is used to achieve the mission and goals. College or school must have an evaluation plan, based on assessment measures, allows for a determination of the degree to which the mission and goals have be achieved. The mission and goals must be related to the vision and needs of the profession of pharmacy to better serve society.

- Standard No. 1: College or School Mission and Goals
- Standard No. 2: Strategic Plan
- Standard No. 3: Evaluation of Achievement of Mission and Goals

Standard No. 1: College or School Mission and Goals

The college or school of pharmacy must have a published statement of its mission, its goals in the areas of education, research and other scholarly activities, service, and pharmacy practice, and its values. The statement must be compatible with the mission of the university in which the college or school operates.' These goals must include fundamental commitments of the college or school to the preparation of students who possess the competencies necessary for the provision of pharmacist-delivered patient care, including medication therapy management services, the advancement of the practice of pharmacy and its contributions to society, the pursuit of research and other scholarly activities, and the assessment and evaluation of desired outcomes.

Guideline 1.1

The college or school's vision for pharmacy practice, research, and education should be aligned with the profession's vision for practice, research, and education.

Guideline 1.2

The college or school should have a vision for education, research, and other scholarly activities that commits faculty and students to fostering innovation through basic and applied research. The research should be related to improving health care outcomes and educational methods. The vision should also include a commitment to participate with other stakeholders in the development of new and improved practice models.

Guideline 1.3

The college or school's mission statement and goals should address the educational philosophy of the professional degree program in preparing graduates with a thorough foundation in the biomedical, pharmaceutical, social/behavioral/adm nistrative, and clinical sciences and their application to practice to enter the pharmacy profession and to contribute positively to its evolution.

Guideline 1.4

The college or school's values should include a stated commitment to a culture that, in general, respects and:

- reflects contemporary pharmacy practice and the vision for its future
- fosters collaboration and good morale among and between administration, faculty, staff, alumni, and students fosters involvement of the college or school in mission-related matters of the pharmacy and health care communities and society in general
- supports meeting the varied needs of student learners and preparing them for the continuum of lifelong education. ('The term "university" includes independent colleges and schools.)

- supports postgraduate professional education and training of pharmacists, unaccredited residencies, fellowships, and graduate programs, including comb] degree options
- supports continuing professional development of faculty, staff, precept(alumni, and other pharmacists
- supports the educational and scholarly maturation and mentoring of new faculi
- fosters innovation, professionalism, ethical behavior, leadership, and scholars
- encourages diversity of both faculty and students
- supports meeting the needs of diverse stakeholders, including fact administrators, staff, students, preceptors, alumni, and others
- attaches importance to scientific advancement
- promotes development of interprofessional learning and collaborative practice
- embraces quality assurance and continuous quality improvement

Guideline 1.5

For new program initiatives and alternate pathways to degree completion, the college school must ensure that:
- The initiatives are consistent with the universities and college or school's miss and goals
- the same commitment is demonstrated to all students, irrespective of prof pathway or geographic location
- resources are allocated in an equitable manner

Standard No. 2: Strategic Plan

The college or school must develop, implement, and regularly revise a strategic plan to facilitate the advancement of its mission and goals. The strategic plan must be developed through an inclusive process that solicits input and review from faculty students, staff, administrators, alumni, and other stakeholders as needed, have support of the university administration, and be disseminated in summary form to key stakeholders.

Guideline 2.1

The strategic plan should address short-term (e.g., 3 to 5 years) strategic goals objectives that are key to the advancement of the college or school's mission and goal.

Guideline 2.2

Strategic goals and objectives should differ from the mission and goals of the college or school, as the latter describe the desired outcomes, while the former are steps to achieve the desired outcomes.

Guideline 2.3

In general, strategic planning should:

- be continuous, with systematic broad-based reflection and revision as needed to meet programmatic and educational needs
- consider the use of external facilitators
- strive for awareness of and commitment to the strategic plan by key stakeholders
- be based on examination of present and projected environmental, professional, and programmatic factors
- assess strengths, weaknesses, opportunities, and threats relevant to the college or school
- be aligned with the university's strategic plan
- identify opportunities for beneficial interactions with other health professions and professionals
- include a review of the college or school's mission statement, goals and values
- prioritize the strategic goals, objectives, and actions
- define measurable outcomes and the processes to assess them
- establish achievable timelines
- identify the resources (e.g., faculty, staff, technical, financial, physical) that need to be allocated
- designate responsibilities
- establish mechanisms for ongoing monitoring and reporting of progress

Guideline 2.4

Substantive changes contemplated by the college or school must be addressed through its strategic planning process. Planning must take into consideration all resources (including financial, human, and physica) required to implement the change and the impact of the change on the existing program. The college or school must notify ACPE in advance of the implementation of any substantive change, allowing sufficient time for evaluation of compliance with standards or the need for additional monitoring.

ACPE's definition of substantive change includes any change in the established mission or goals of the institution; the addition or deletion of courses, pathways, or programs that represent a significant departure in either content or method of delivery from those that were offered during the program's previous accreditation cycle (e.g., a nontraditional doctor of pharmacy program or development of a joint delivery of program agreement); a substantial change in enrollment; a substantial change in the number of clock or credit hours required for successful completion of the program; a significant change in the length of the program; the establishment of an additional geographic location at which the program is offered; and any other changes that the dean feels require notification to ACPE.

Guideline 2.5

A substantive change that involves new program initiatives (such as alternate program pathways to degree completion, including geographically dispersed campuses and distance-learning activities) should result from documented needs and be included in the strategic planning process, ensuring adequate lead time for development.

Standard No. 3: Evaluation of Achievement of Mission and Goals

The college or school must establish and implement an evaluation plan that assesses achievement of the mission and goals. The evaluation must measure the extent to which the desired outcomes of the professional degree program (including assessments of student learning and evaluation of the effectiveness of the curriculum) are being achieved. Likewise, the extent to which the desired outcomes of research and other scholarly activities, service, and pharmacy practice programs are being achieved must be measured. The college or school must use the analysis of process and outcome measures for continuous development and improvement of the professional degree program.

Guideline 3.1

The evaluation plan must describe a continuous and systematic process of evaluation covering all aspects of the college or school and the accreditation standards. The plan must be evidence-based and embrace the principles and methodologies of continuous quality improvement. As a component of the strategic planning process, the evaluation plan and the specific assessments should be reviewed for completeness, appropriateness, and effectiveness by internal and external stakeholders.

Guideline 3.2

In general, the evaluation plan should describe the:

- desired outcomes of the professional degree program (including assessments of student learning and evaluation of the effectiveness of the curriculum), research and other scholarly activities, service, and pharmacy practice programs
- process and outcome assessments that will be measured and evaluated, and with what frequency
- individual(s) responsible for data collection, analysis, and dissemination
- parties that will be responsible to receive and be authorized to act on the findings manner by which resultant changes (e.g., revisions in the curriculum or modifications of faculty and student policies and procedures) will be implemented, evaluated, documented, and communicated
- colleges or schools, in addition to all ACPE-accredited programs, that will be used for peer comparison, if any, and the basis for their selection

Guideline 3.3

In general, the assessments employed in the evaluation plan should:

- include defined formative and summative measures,
- involve the full range of relevant internal and external stakeholders,
- permit anonymous input and provide for collective analyses of findings be used to evaluate trends over time
- include, where available, standardized or common instruments and data, such as those available through the American Association of Colleges of Pharmacy (AACP) and the National Association of Boards of Pharmacy (NABP), to allow comparisons with other accredited professional degree programs and peer colleges and schools

Guideline 3.4

The college or school should make available to key stakeholders, on an annual basis, the major findings and actions resulting from its evaluation plan through, for example, it's written annual report or its Web site.

Guideline 3.5

The evaluation plan must include assessments that will allow comparison and establishment of comparability of alternative program pathways to degree completion, including geographically dispersed campuses and distance-learning activities.

A formative assessment measure is one taken before the activity or program is completed or repeated; an example would be a student's midpoint grade in a course. Formative assessments should allow for corrective actions. A summative assessment measure is one taken at the conclusion of an activity or program; an example would be a student's final grade in a course. Summative assessments help define the degree to which outcomes have been attained.

It is to be further emphasized that standards which were effective from 2007, have been further modified, released in 2014 and are proposed to be implemented from 2016. This indicates dynamic nature of both the curriculum and the accreditation criteria.

A lot of guidelines are available for Indian decision-makers related to Pharmacy education based on the American document. The important guideline is the process of consultation with all stakeholders in most serious manner giving them enough time to consider the suggested changes. However still more important guideline is to visualize future of Pharmacy at least a decade in advance to identify The Foundations of Pharmacy Practice, How Pharmacists Will Practice, and How Pharmacy Practice Will Benefit Society. Having identified these basic facts, the exercise of Curriculum Design should be undertaken at a national level and then appropriate advice should be given to Universities to frame the syllabi.

Contours of responsibilities with respect to Medical profession should be well defined so that there is clarity about what is expected of a pharmacist so far as pharmaceutical care of patients is concerned. The curriculum can be framed in such a manner that independent professional in a pharmacist can be objectively evolved. Once clarity about professional responsibilities is sorted, accreditation system can be worked out based on standards and related guidelines. If the process for Future Vision for Indian Pharmacists starts in 2015, we can certainly modify real face of Indian pharmacists, at least by 2025.

Chapter 7...

ACCREDITATION OF PHARMACY CONTINUING EDUCATION IN USA

ACPE prescribes separate criteria for continuing pharmacy education (CPE). It is defined as "A structured educational activity designed or intended to support the continuing development of pharmacists and/or pharmacy technicians to maintain and enhance their competence. Continuing pharmacy education (CPE) should promote problem-solving and critical thinking and be applicable to the practice of pharmacy." In USA, pharmacy technician is an independent professional entity.

Twelve standards for the purpose of CPE have been described by ACPE under four headings; viz.

- Content of Continuing Pharmacy Education Activities
- Delivery of CPE Activities.
- Assessment. and
- Evaluation.

It is to be emphasized that for professional education, continuing education is important because of new addition of knowledge has inevitable impact on the profession. In case of pharmacy education, addition of new drugs, reports of adverse reactions from time to time, regulatory changes, and all other new information on drugs needs to be communicated to all related stakeholders. Continuing education is the only medium for the transfer of information.

The details regarding adoption and revision are as follows.

Adoption: June 20, 2007

Released: October 5, 2007

Effective: January 1, 2009

Version 2: Released March, 2014

The standards are as follows.

Content of Continuing Pharmacy Education Activities

- Standard 1: Goal and Mission of the CPE Program
- Standard 2: Educational Needs Assessment

- Standard 3: Continuing Pharmacy Education Activities
- Standard 4: CPE Activity Objectives
- Standard 5: Standards for Commercial Support

Delivery of CPE Activities

- Standard 6: Faculty
- Standard 7: Teaching and Learning Methods
- Standard 8: Educational Materials

Assessment

- Standard 9: Assessment of Learning
- Standard 10: Assessment Feedback

Evaluation

- Standard 11: Evaluation of CPE Activities
- Standard 12: Achievement and Impact of CPE Mission and Goals

The Accreditation Council for Pharmacy Education is the national agency for the accreditation of professional degree programs in pharmacy and providers of continuing pharmacy education. ACPE was established in 1932 for the accreditation of professional degree programs in pharmacy. In 1975 its scope was broadened to include accreditation of providers of continuing pharmacy education

Standard 1: Goal and Mission of the CPE Program

The provider must develop a CPE goal and mission statement that defines the basis and intended outcomes for the majority of educational activities the provider offers

Standard 2: Educational Needs Assessment

The provider must develop CPE activities based on a multifaceted process where educational needs are prospectively identified

Standard 3: Continuing Pharmacy Education Activities

The provider must structure each CPE activity to meet the knowledge-, application- and/or practice-based educational needs of pharmacists and technicians.

Standard 4: CPE Activity Objectives

The provider must develop objectives for each CPE activity that define what the pharmacists and technicians should be able to do at the completion of each CPE activity.

Standard 5: Standards for Commercial Support

The provider must plan all CPE activities independent of commercial interest. The educational content must be presented with full disclosure and equitable balance.

Appropriate topics and learning activities must be distinguished from topics and learning activities which are promotional or appear to be intended for the purpose of endorsing either a specific commercial drug, device or other commercial product (as contrasted with the generic product/drug entity and its contents or the general therapeutic area it addresses), or a specific commercial service (as contrasted with the general service area and/or the aspects or problems of professional practice it addresses).

Standard 6: Faculty

The provider must communicate and collaborate with CPE activity faculty regarding the identified educational needs, intended audience, objectives, active participation, and learning assessments for each CPE activity

Standard 7: Teaching and Learning Methods

The provider must assure that all CPE activities include active participation and involvement of the pharmacist and technician.

Standard 8: Educational Materials

The provider must offer educational materials for each CPE activity that will enhance participants' understanding of the content and foster applications to pharmacy practice.

Standard 9: Assessment of Learning

The provider in collaboration with faculty must include learning assessments in each CPE activity to allow pharmacists and technicians to assess their achievement of the learned content. Completion of a learning assessment is required for CPE credit.

Standard 10: Assessment Feedback

The provider must ensure learner assessment feedback is provided to participants in an appropriate, timely, and constructive manner

Standard 11: Evaluation of CPE Activity

Providers must develop and conduct evaluations of each CPE activity. The evaluations must allow pharmacists and technicians to provide feedback on the following items:

- applicability of the CPE activity to meet their educational needs
- achievement of each stated objective
- quality of faculty

- usefulness of educational material
- effectiveness of teaching and learning methods, including active learning
- appropriateness of learning assessment activities
- perceptions of bias or commercialism

Standard 12: Achievement and Impact of Mission and Goals

Providers must establish and implement evaluation plans that assess achievement and impact of stated mission and goals (Standard 1). They must use this information for continuous development and improvement of the CPE program.

Detailing of two standards and relevant guidance related to continuing education is presented below.

One

Standard 3: Continuing Pharmacy Education Activities

The provider must structure each CPE activity to meet the knowledge-, application- and/or practice-based educational needs of pharmacists and technicians.

Guidance:

Knowledge-based CPE activity:

These CPE activities should be designed primarily for pharmacists and technicians to acquire factual knowledge. This information must be based on evidence as accepted in the literature by the health care professions. The minimum credit for these activities is 15 minutes or 0.25 contact hour.

Application-based CPE activity:

These CPE activities should be designed primarily for pharmacists and technicians to apply the information learned in the time frame allotted. The information must be based on evidence as accepted in the literature by the health care professions. The minimum credit for these activities is 60 minutes or one contact hour.

Practice-based CPE activity:

These CPE activities should be designed primarily for pharmacists and technicians to systematically acquire specific knowledge, skills, attitudes, and performance behaviors that expand or enhance practice competencies. The information within the practice-based CPE activity must be based on evidence as accepted in the literature by the health care professions. The formats of these CPE activities should include a didactic component and a practice component. The minimum credit for these activities is 15 contact hours.

Providers are not required to offer all three activity types. The CPE activities should be consistent with the provider's mission and appropriate to meet the identified pharmacist and technician needs.

Providers are encouraged to guide pharmacists and technicians to the best combination of CPE activities to meet their practice needs

Two

Standard 9: Assessment of Learning

The provider in collaboration with faculty must include learning assessments in each CPE activity to allow pharmacists and technicians to assess their achievement of the learned content. Completion of a learning assessment is required for CPE credit.

Guidance

The provider may select formal and informal techniques for assessment of learning. Informal techniques typically involve participant discussions. Formal techniques, such as tests and quizzes, are typically individualized, written, and graded. The assessment should be consistent with the identified CPE activity objectives (Standard 4) and activity type (Standard 3).

Knowledge-based CPE activity:

Each CPE activity in this category must include assessment questions structured to determine recall of facts.

Application-based CPE activity:

Each CPE activity in this category must include case studies structured to address application of the principles learned.

Practice-based CPE activity:

Each CPE activity in this category must include formative and summative assessments that demonstrate that the pharmacists and technicians achieved the stated objectives.

Thus it is amply evident that ACPE has given due importance to accreditation of continuing education. It needs to be emphasized that if continuing education is treated as seriously as that of core education, then the standard of professional integrity will enhance to a large extent. In Indian context, it is to be noted that PCI is considering declaring continuing education as mandatory to preserve the registration as pharmacist. Few modules or patient counseling have been included in the training programs of pharmacists. If a mechanism of accreditation of short and long-term continuing education programs is developed in India, then linking credits earned through continuing education to professional development will be very meaningful. If PCI takes this point seriously, then earning few credits of continuing education either annually or once in two/three years can be linked to continuation of registration as pharmacists. This then will be a perpetual long-standing event and will help in promoting image of the pharmacy profession. Putting self- imposed features is a characteristic of a profession and divides it between trade and profession. When questions are being raised as to "Whether pharmacy is a trade or profession?", accreditation of continuing education in pharmacy can go a long way in validating it as a profession. A similar exercise can be done for teaching profession and few minimum credits of accreditated continuing education should be considered mandatory for every teacher in order to continue University recognition of the teacher.

Chapter 8

QUALITY ASSURANCE IN GLOBAL PHARMACY INSTITUTIONS

The international forum for Quality Assurance of Pharmacy Education in association with International Pharmaceutical Federation (FIP) has published a document on "A Global Framework for Quality Assurance of Pharmacy Education" in August, 2008. The document has been divided into three subsections.

- Section A: Quality Assurance in Pharmacy Education.
- Section B: The Quality Assurance Agency.
- Section C: Quality criteria for Pharmacy Education.

The introductory part of the document emphasizes global need to build capacity and assure quality. With a wide variety in practices related to health-care systems all over the world, it needs to be emphasized that healthcare targets cannot be realized until capacity is built in the healthcare system. A primary focus should be placed on development of an adequate and appropriate workforce, along with the academic and institutional infrastructure to deliver the required competency-based education and training. However while training such work force a robust system of maintaining quality of the system should not be overlooked. The quality of education can be assured only with appropriate structures, processes and outcomes built within the system.

A forum has been established under academic section of the FIP. The objectives of the forum are:

- To promote excellence in education for the profession of pharmacy
- To provide an international forum for information exchange, collaboration and cooperation in the area of quality assurance of pharmacy education for entry-to practice degree programs, continuing education (CE) and continuing professional development (CPD)
- To facilitate and promote communication between individuals , agencies, associations, and other bodies actively involved in, or interested in, quality assurance of pharmacy education with a view to
  - o The establishment of systems of quality assurance in countries where no such formal system exist.
- The continuous quality improvement of existing systems of quality assurance.

Section A: Quality Assurance in Pharmacy Education

A Vision for Pharmacy Practice and Education

India is a country with diverse population with various lifestyles and practices with respect to health. As a result needs of pharmacy practice and education are unique. In fact pharmacy practice is relatively new to Indian society with an experience of nearly two decades. The Indian system of pharmacy practice is primarily originating from Australian experiences through collaboration with few pharmacy colleges in India.

Needs of society

Globally needs of the society change from county to country. Accordingly, the role of pharmacists changes in different counties. FIP has published two documents related to pharmacy practice.

1. Standards for quality of pharmacy services (1993, 1997)
2. Statement of professional standards on pharmaceutical care (1998)

As medication therapy has become more complex, more accessible, and used in more diverse and ageing patients, patient safety issue and accountability for outcomes of therapy have become a greater focus of attention. Consumers are demanding higher standards and seeking assurance of quality.

In India, prescriptions are issued by physicians based on diagnosis of the disease. The prescriptions are taken to pharmacist and dispensing of the drugs is performed by pharmacists. Presently the major job of pharmacists is involved in dispensing of drugs only. Counseling of patients on interactions between drugs, adverse drug reactions, advice about food restrictions, if any, and individualization of dosages based on the conditions of patients is not being taken care of by pharmacist to a large extent. The patients have to depend much on physicians for this advice. Physicians give very less time with the patient for the purpose of counseling on issues related to drugs. This gap can be very well fitted by pharmacist. For this propose, pharmacist need a special training and close interaction with the patients along with a functional knowledge about the disease. All this content of pharmacy education and practice should be reflected in the curriculum of B. Pharm.

Development of vision for pharmacy practice and education

The manpower of pharmacy students can be effectively used for better health care in India. For this purpose roles and responsibilities of pharmacists in the delivery of health care services should be precisely identified. Further, the competencies required to carry out these roles and responsibilities should be clearly articulated. It is necessary to consider the level, model and duration of education and training to achieve the identified competencies before entering the practice and maintain and enhance them thereafter. The curricular content and practical experiences should be designed in such a manner that the educational outcomes meet the desired competencies.

It is to be emphasized that strategic discussion has no role in isolation. Unless all stakeholders are involved in the discussion and take an active interest in implementation of the concept, a meaningful outcome will not result. It is necessary to have a consensus on the objectives of the profession and vision has to be successfully articulated, pursued, and achieved. The discussions should be conducted in the context of national needs and priorities and should take in to account all required resources and the implications of the proposed changes. A clear, appropriate, realistic and achievable national vision for education and practice should be developed through a collaborative effort.

The stakeholders in pharmacy practice are patients, doctors, pharmacists, manufactures and distributors of drugs. All of them should be involved to have a consensus on the objective of pharmacy profession. The draft objective can be 'ready accessibility of quality drugs at affordable prices'. In addition rational use of drugs can be an added objective. To meet these objectives, understanding common consumers in India is essential. Nearly 40% of the population is below poverty line and their financial condition is such that if they spend more on drugs, they have limited recourses for food. Hence affordability is the central issue about availability of rational drugs.

The most important point is to have a correlation between education, regulation and practice. None of these components are static. Hence dynamic relation between these components has to be maintained such that the balance between them is not disturbed. Any gap between these components result in to creating a disconnect, which may lead to tensions, dissatisfaction, or frustration. The following figure (Figure 1) depicts the inter-relation effectively.

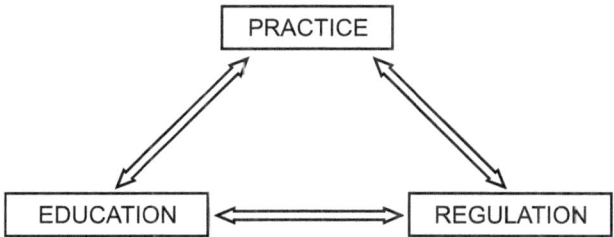

Fig. 1 : Dynamic relations between Practice, Education and Reguations

Stakeholder involvement in assuring and advancing pharmacy education

As much as all the stakeholders should be involved in development and adoption of the vision for the profession, they should all be equally involved in the process of quality assurance of the system as well. Al sectors should have same right in arguing and finalizing the statement. Professional organizations like Indian Pharmaceutical Association, Association of Pharmaceutical Teachers of India, All India Chemists and Druggists association, Voluntary Health Association of India should take pride and ownership in the education of future practitioners and care for assuring quality outcomes.

The Philosophy and Propose of Quality Assurance in Pharmacy Education
Identifying the stakeholders

A list of stakeholders is indicated in the figure 2.

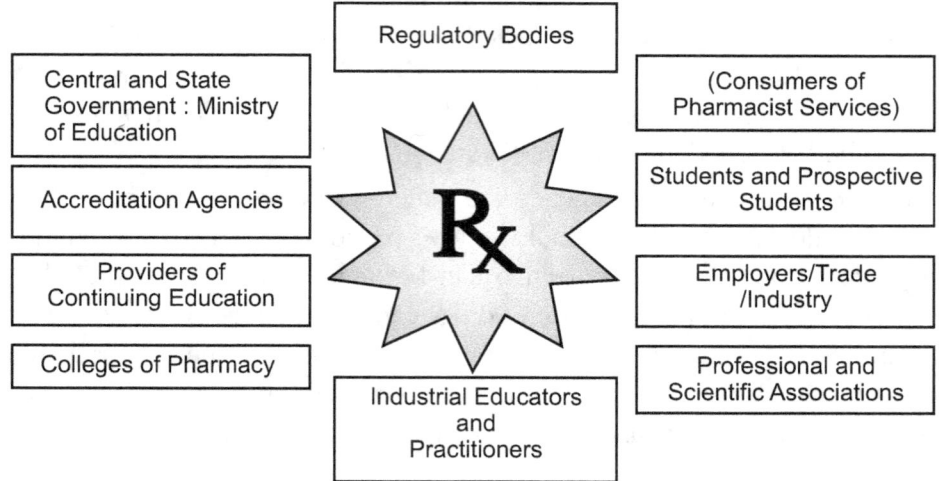

Fig. 2 : Stackholders in the quality assurance of pharmacy education

From a political and regulatory standpoint, additional specific authorities responsible for practice of pharmacy have the duty to protect the interests and wellbeing of the public. This requires assurance that pharmacists receive appropriate education and training and are competent to deliver the range of services permitted in their scope of practice. Completion of approved program of study is a standard prerequisite for licensure or registration as a pharmacist. As a major contributor to the financing of higher education, governments have a reason to desire quality outcomes of their investment in education for national development. In India, National Board of Accreditation (NBA) has the responsibility for quality assurance of pharmacy education.

Students, as consumers, do have an interest in quality of education along with their parents. As the primary recipients of education, students' input is essential component of the quality assurance process. Still feedback from students and its evaluation alone cannot provide the full scope of required perspectives. The interests of members of the faculty, staff, and administrators as well as other affiliated organizations or individuals should also be protected and advanced through an effective quality assurance system. Especially greater attention should be given to interests of other programs at an institution, which are subjected to external quality assurance or accreditation process. Any institution offering a program in pharmacy, may it be a affiliated college or an University department, can be benefitted from a standardized, external evaluation of their program. The professional as a whole, as it seeks to advance and better serve society and its members, relies heavily on the quality assurance system to maintain the integrity of the educational process and ensure the competence, professionalism, and leadership of future practitioners. This is of special importance in constantly changing needs of the society, either because of technological advances or because of changing life styles.

Finally, it is the common public or average consumers of the wide ranging services provided directly or indirectly by pharmacist – that benefits most from the system that assures the quality of education and training provided to pharmacists. It is through policy and practice that members of the public are involved in the quality assurance of education and regulation of practice of health care professionals. Thus quality assurance of education in pharmacy practice standardizes the system of education on one hand and ensures better service to patients on the other hand.

Different models of quality assurance

Indian government has traditionally been involved in the quality assurance of education for health care professionals through a board for accreditation. Professional association can be another alternative. In any case functional autonomy in decision making and operations is vital to maintain integrity of the system. Private accreditation agencies working under the umbrella of higher education system can be another alternative. Interference from the government in the functioning of accreditation agencies should be strictly restricted.

Concepts and elements of quality assurance

While quality assurance might often be perceived as a system of external review by an entity not directly involved in the process or institution being evaluated, a comprehensive quality assurance systems should incorporate many more elements and promote a specific culture within the institute whose process or program in being evaluated. One of the key foundations of any quality assurance systems is *the standards or criteria* by which quality is defined. In other words these criteria decide the highest bar to which institution should reach in terms of content and processes.

All quality assurance systems should be based on well-articulated standards which clearly state their purpose and expectation. Such standards should have following characteristics:

- The standards should be developed through a collaborative and transparent process involving all stakeholders.
- The standards should be endorsed across the profession
- They should be evidence – based
- They should be validated through reliable measures and outcomes
- They should be publicly disclosed; and
- They should be reviewed and updated periodically to ensure applicability

National standards should permit inclusion of local innovations and mission – related differences at the institution level. (Figure 3)

Fig. 3: Quality Assurance and Quality Advancement

The objective of a quality assurance system is not to have uniformity in functioning of all pharmacy colleges. In fact it should assure that specific outcomes are achieved and core quality elements are established and maintained to support the achievement of desired outcomes. Three main areas viz. *outcomes, Structure and process* are the main pillars of quality. (Figure 4)

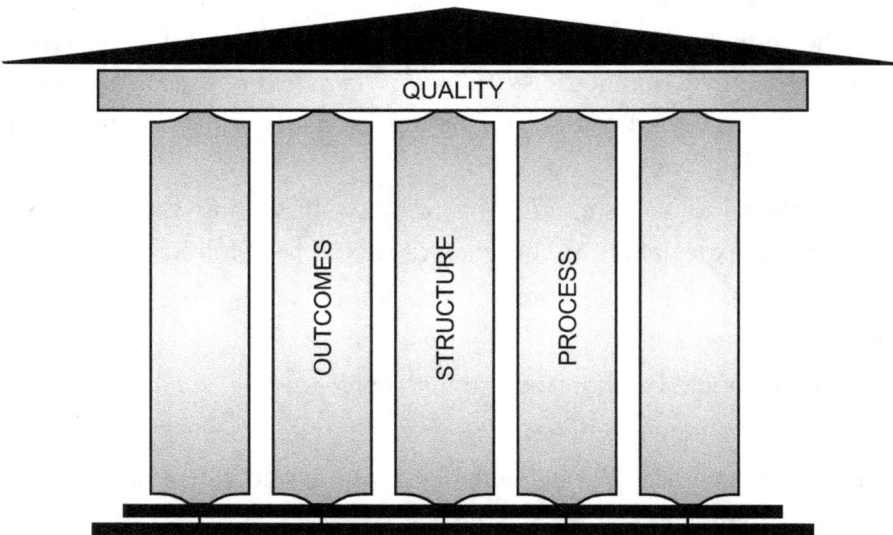

Fig. 4: The Pillars of Quality

In addition to these three main pillars the quality assurance systems and agency should have rigorous and stringently – applied policies and procedures which assure consistency, impartiality, fairness, and integrity of evaluation and decision-making process. Such policies and procedures should be developed by consulting all stakeholders in a transparent manner. Subsequently the standards should be publicly displayed on the website of the agency.

External evaluation is preferable through a 'peer reviews' process, by involving experts having qualifications, expertise and experience which is commensurate with the process of assurance of quality of educational system. Practitioners working on the field may also be involved to add practical components. Quality assurance should involve initial evaluation with periodic and regular follow up to ensure ongoing compliance with existing or revised standards or criteria, in view of constantly changing professional education and dynamic environmental changes. Usually a period of one, three or five years may be given for an accredited institute for its continuation. If more deficiencies are observed, the duration of accreditation may be less.

Increasingly, quality assurance systems are incorporating a greater element of self-assessment, whereby institutions undertake a comprehensive, broad – based exercise in introspection to make their own assessment against established standards and criteria. By following these practices, institutes are encouraged to promote a cultural assessment and continuous self – improvement on its own. Thus the institute assumes responsibility on its own. It is expected that the quality assurance system should work as a partner, facilitator, and collaborator rather than being a 'bossing' entity only to identify weakness of the system.

Finally, the policies and procedures of the quality assurance agencies should provide for a system of appeal in case of unexpected outcomes. Through the process of appeal, the decisions or actions of the agency can be challenged or questioned. The system has to be transparent to convince the institute about evaluation criteria and its objectivity.

Section B: The Quality Assurance Agency

It is necessary that key aspects of structure, governance, policies and procedures which should be considered while establishing or restructuring a quality assuring agency be considered. It is emphasized that the systems of government and quality assurance of pharmacy education are diverse because of wide-ranging topics being covered in the process of education. Outline for such a system is proposed here in the Indian context.

Structure and purpose of the Quality Assurance Agency

Mission, Terms of reference, and Scope of operations: All stake holders should be consulted before drafting these contents. Similarly draft should be circulated to all stakeholders before giving a final shape to the document. Experts from industry should be consulted seriously to incorporate their needs. Needs of industries change with time; hence constant dialogue with industries be maintained.

Legal/Statutory status : The quality assurance agency should have statutory status offered by Ministry of Human Resources or Ministry of Health and Family Welfare. Right now,

National Board of Accreditation (NBA) or National Assessment and Accreditation Council (NAAC) are performing the job quality assurance of education and they have statutory status from Central Govt. of India through Ministry of Human Resources Development (MHRD).

Recognition, authority, and accountability : The relevant questions are as follows :

- Who has given recognition to the agency?
- What mandate and authority does it have?
- To whom is it accountable?
- What requirements and criteria must the agency meet?

Answers to these questions are incorporated in the documents of NBA, and NAAC respectively.

Degree of autonomy in decision making : The agency should have full autonomy based on international criteria about standards, policies and procedures to be satisfied by educational institutions and all these should be documented well after consulting all stakeholders. There should not be any undue influence from any quarters about design or implementation of the criteria.

Influence of market forces : Ability of the agency to influence or be influenced by the market forces needs to be established and clearly understood by all stakeholders. The market forces in case of pharmacy education involves pharmaceutical industries and community pharmacy.

Relationship with other organizations and stakeholders : Professional organizations like Indian Pharmaceutical Association, Association of Pharmaceutical Teacher's of India, Indian Drug Manufacturer's Association, Organization of Pharmaceutical Producers of India should be interacted with by the Quality Assurance agency like NBA or NAAC in order to fix parameters for evaluation .

Governance and decision making:

- **Composition:** Composition of the decision - making body should be such that representatives of all stakeholders should be available in it. Educators, regulators and practitioners are the main stakeholders.
- **Officers:** it is important to decide whether officers will be elected or appointed. It is preferable that based on the competence, officers should be selected by experts and then appointed by the right authority.
- **Public input:** it is necessary that public views should be considered. Nongovernmental organizations (NGOs) are the right source for public input. Such NGOs should be necessarily involved in the process of education.
- **Criteria for appointment or selection of members:** Discretion of political authority should not be the basis of appointment/selection of members. Qualifications and

experience in the field of education should be basis of appointment/selection of the members.

- **Terms of office of members:** A period of 3 to 5 years is usual term of the office of members.

Funding

It is necessary to identify the source of funding for the agency. Usually fees are charged by the agency to the educational institutes whose quality is to be assessed. The quantum of fees should be announced well in advance, applied fairly and consistently, and constituents should be notified about changes if any, as soon as they are decided.

Policies and procedures

Board/committee/council operations:

4.1.1   The key components of the evaluation procedure should be established, communicated and consistently applied.

4.1.2   When meetings will be held and how they will be conducted should be established, communicated and consistently followed.

4.1.3   The criteria on which decisions are based should be articulate and consistently and fairly applied.

Evaluation/recognition/approval

4.2.1   Requirements for initial application for evaluation/recognition/approval should be clearly stated. If the educational institute needs to satisfy certain minimum prerequisites, these should be announced well in advance and fairly and consistently applied.

4.2.2   The stages of evaluation/recognition/approval, including requirements for progression through different stages should be clearly stated. This will primarily apply to new programs or institutions.

4.2.3   Evaluation/recognition/approval cycle should be stated. Once approved, what is the standard duration for which the approval will continue should be indicated. A period of one/three/five years has to be spelt out. Minimum and maximum duration between comprehensive evaluations should be indicated.

4.2.4   Requirements for maintenance of recognition /approval, including self – assessment and other reporting, annual monitoring data, ad hoc on-site evaluation visits/ audits should be clearly identified. Any additional requirements, over and above the comprehensive on-site evaluation visits need to be clearly defined and communicated.

4.2.5   Consequences of non-compliance with standards/quality criteria should be established and clearly communicated to educational institutes or program which is potentially affected.

Public Disclosure

4.3.1   Published standards or quality criteria, policies and procedures should be readily accessible to any interested person or stakeholder.

4.3.2   Which decisions or actions of Board/committee/council will be disclosed publicly should be indicated. Minutes of the meetings are usually preferred. How and which information is to be disclosed to whom should be clearly indicated.

4.3.3   Recognition/approval status of the educational institutions or the program should be publicly disclosed.

Policies and Procedures

4.4.1   Confidentiality: Certain sensitive information needs to be protected and need not come in public domain. Policies and procedures deciding which information is to be treated as confidential and how it is to be dealt with needs to be defined in writing.

4.4.2   Conflict of Interest : What is 'conflict of interest ' needs to be defined by an appropriate regulation. Anybody having conflict of interest has to be excluded from the important decision-making activities of the institute. Policies and procedures must be established to identify identification and occurrence of a conflict of interest. Active interest in activities of competing institutions and possible leakage of sensitive information to them constitutes a conflict of interest.

4.4.3   Selection and training of persons used in evaluation : The persons involved in evaluation need to be appropriately trained. Qualifications, experience and background of the persons to be trained should be defined. The concerned persons should get training in standards, policies, procedures and method of evaluation prior to involvement in evaluation. Training should be linked to practical aspects.

4.4.4   Substantive change : If there is any major change in curriculum or program, then policies and procedures should be established and implemented to ensure that the agency is given adequate notice of the proposed major changes. Impact of the change should be adequately evaluated and appropriate actions should be taken by the institute.

4.4.5   Appeals: If the quality-assurance agency takes any decision about which the institution is unhappy, then the process of appeal or arbitration should be established and communicated to all stakeholders. The doubts raised by the institution should have objective basis.

4.4.6   Complaints against the quality assurance agency, a school or program : Unlike appeal, if there are any legitimate complaints against actions taken by the Quality-assurance agency, then the process of complaints and arbitration, if applicable, should be established and communicated to all stakeholders.

4.4.7   **Revision/updating of standards :** A policy , procedure and likely schedule for review and revision of star.dards should be established and communicated to key stakeholders; The need for revision of standards originate from major changes on the field; hence input from key stakeholders is invited, facilitated and taken into consideration by the agency.

4.4.8   **Safeguards for students :** Unfortunately if the recognition or approval of the program is withdrawn, then the rights of students, options and contingency measures should be established in consultation with all stakeholders and clearly communicated. Transfer of students to another recognized institut.on with transfer of credits is the right way of safeguarding interest of students.

Section C: Quality Criteria for Pharmacy Education

There are three important criteria relevant to quality assurance of education. The criteria are outcomes, structure and process. These criteria are a broader framework that provide guidance for quality assurance. The criteria serve as a tool to es-abl:sh quality assurance system. Each of the criteria are discussed here.

OUTCOMES

The outcomes are further discussed under two headings. First issue is defining educational outcomes and competencies and second issue is evaluation of achievement of outcomes.

Educational outcomes and competencies:

Quality assurance standards of Pharmacy education should be competency-based. The competencies can be conveniently divided into pharmacy-based competencies and general competencies. Broadly pharmacy–based competencies can be subdivided into following three categories:

- Patient-care services at the individual and population levels.
- Management of systems and resources. and
- Promotion of public health.

General competencies applicable to all health professionals include:

- Ethical, caring and evidence-based practice.
- Cultural competence.
- Application of quality improvement principles.
- Use of information technologies. And
- Working in interdisciplinary and interprofessional teams

The competencies should be identified through profession-wide consensus, so that national vision for pharmacy practice and education is reflected in them. The competencies should be appropriate to current and future national healthcare needs with regard to services provided by pharmacists. Unfortunately national vision for pharmacy practice and education and competencies required by pharmacists to attain them are ill-defined in India. As a result there is no correlation between educational outcomes and competencies. The autonomy of Universities further create a diversity in curricula.

It is expected that pharmacy practitioners from all settings, regulators, educators and consumers of pharmacy services should all contribute to the identification of professional competencies. The competencies should be used to guide the development of student learning outcome expectations for the curriculum. Competency-curriculum-correlation is missing in Indian curricula.

Realizing that no professional degree program can anticipate all of its future requirements, pharmacists will have to be continuous learners. Hence educational outcome-statements should incorporate the development of the skills and attitudes necessary to become self-directed, lifelong learners.

Standards established by the quality assurance agency may be indicated either at a high level or at a detailed level. Globally the concept of "Seven Star Pharmacist "has been acknowledged by International Pharmaceutical Federation (FIP) and World Health Organization (WHO). It emphasizes on seven roles of pharmacists: 1. Care giver; 2. Decision maker; 3. Communicator; 4. Leader; 5. Manager; 6. Life-long learner; and 7. Teacher. These seven roles can be broadly considered in formulating educational outcomes and competency statements.

Evaluation of achievement of mission-related outcomes

It is necessary to evaluate student learning and curricular effectiveness. The institute should develop and undertake assessment activities to collect data regarding attainment of desired student learning outcomes. The assessment activities should employ a variety of valid and reliable measures systematically and sequentially throughout the program of B.Pharm. or Pharm. D. The institute should use the results obtained from analysis and interpretation of assessment data to improve student learning and the achievement of the professional competencies based on the assessment data.

The institute should systematically evaluate and validate its curricular structure, content, organization, teaching and learning methodologies and outcomes. The institute should use the results of such evaluation and data from assessment of student learning for continuous improvement of the curriculum and its delivery. Curricular change based on feedback about students is a continuous life-long process. In addition, what applies for curricular change also equally applies to other mission-related activities. Feedback about assessment for such activities should also be taken from the field.

2. STRUCTURE

2.1 Mission, goals and values of the institute:

The institute/ college of Pharmacy should have a statement which expresses its mission, goals, and values in the areas of teaching, research and scholarly activity, service to the community, contribution to Pharmacy practice, and advancement of the profession. The mission and goals should reflect the national objectives of the profession, vision for pharmacy practice and education and ensure that graduates are properly educated and trained to deliver pharmacy services which can meet current as well as future needs of the pharmacy profession. The mission and goals should reflect a commitment to continuous quality improvement. The goals should be S.M.A.R.T. indicating specific, measurable, achievable, relevant and time specific so that achievement of goals can be evaluated at any point of time. A University or a college may have some unique aspects to its mission and objectives based on location or expertise. However it is cautioned that specialty of any college /University should not compromise the achievement of the required programmatic outcomes and compliance with quality criteria. Based on assessment about achievement about mission and goals, follow up action should be initiated.

The management of the college should strive to provide an environment which promotes ethical and professional behavior and harmonious relationship with administrators, faculty, staff and students. All these stakeholders should be committed to developing professionalism and fostering leadership in students and to serve as the role model for students. The college should support the participation of administration, faculty, staff and students in local and national pharmacy, scientific and other professional organizations like Indian Pharmaceutical Association, Association of Pharmaceutical Teachers of India, Indian Drug Manufacturer's Association etc.

The college is expected to implement such strategies and programs which will broaden the professional horizons of students in areas like scientific inquiry, scholarly concern for the profession, the relevance, methodology and value of research, in postgraduate and doctoral training.

2.2   Organization, administration, leadership, and communication

2.2.1 The Director/ Principal of the college.

The Director/ Principal of the college should provide leadership to the college and assume primary responsibility for ensuring the quality of the pharmacy program. The Director/ Principal should have appropriate qualifications and experience to provide leadership in all mission-related areas , ensure effective communication with all stakeholders, secure adequate resources , and be able to unite and inspire administrators, faculty, staff and students towards achievement of the mission and goals. The leadership and effectiveness of the Director/Principal should be evaluated on a regular basis using a broad-based approach.

2.2.2 Organizational Structure

The college should be organized and staffed to facilitate the accomplishment of its mission and goals. Within the ambit of university framework, members of the college administration should have defined lines of authority and responsibility, foster organizational unit development and collegiality, and allocate resources appropriately. The efficiency and effectiveness of the organizational structure should be evaluated to ensure that it properly supports the achievement of the mission and goals. The overall mission, goals and objectives should be subdivided into conventional departments like pharmaceutics, pharmaceutical chemistry, pharmacology, pharmacognosy, pharmacy practice etc. Objectives of individual faculty and the departments should be aligned with the mission and goals of the college. The effectiveness of each organizational unit should be evaluated on the basis of its goals and objectives and its contribution to the professional program and its overall mission. The periodic review of heads of the departments and principal should include input from other administrators, faculty, staff and students.

2.2.3 Committees

Faculty committees should be constituted to ensure achievement of objectives. Working of these committees and faculty meetings should be part of the system of governance of the college. Few representative committees are indicated here: Curriculum committee, Assessment committee, strategic planning committee, research committee, admissions committee, placement committee, library committee, purchase committee etc wherever appropriate, committees should include staff, students, alumni and pharmacy practitioners.

2.3   Collaborative relationship

2.3.1 Within the university

Whenever the college is affiliated to a university it is essential that cordial and collaborative working relationship exists between the college and university administration, and between different colleges and or departments of the universities. This is to ensure that the college advances its mission and goals and receives adequate financial physical resources for teaching and research, faculty, staff, students, library, technology, administrative resources and training sites other than the college. Within the policies and procedures of the universities the college should have enough autonomy to decide its own policies, procedures and operations towards its mission, goals and objectives. Following areas are indicative where autonomy should be exercised by the colleges: programmatic evaluation, development and delivery of the curriculum, development of college policies and procedures, student enrolment, student admission and progression: and faculty and staff recruitment, retention, development and evaluation.

In the existing Indian situation system the university decides the entire curriculum and the college's do not have autonomy in the curricular component.

2.3.2 Other collaborative relationships

The college without full support of university should develop collaborative relationship and partnerships with stakeholders outside the university to support and advance its mission and goals. Few examples of areas of collaboration are indicated:

- Interaction with Industries.
- Pharmacy practice.
- Community service.
- Community research and related scholarly activities.

Various stake holders need to be involved for collaboration eg. Employers, regulatory agencies, professional bodies, scientific societies, research institutions, community and patient groups and other similar institutions. In addition to this the college should have active relationships with health and science related sectors of society and government.

2.4 The curriculum

The curriculum of the professional degree program should be designed in such a way that it prepares graduates with competencies which are needed by them to enter in pharmacy practice of different designs and contribute to the profession of pharmacy throughout the career. The curriculum should provide a thorough knowledge base in following areas

- Biomedical Sciences.
- Pharmaceutical Sciences.
- Social Sciences.
- Clinical Sciences.
- Behavioral Sciences and administrative aspects.
- Field experiences

The components should be organized in a integrative manner to apply, reinforce and advance the knowledge, the skills, attitudes, behaviors and values developed through the other components of the curriculum. Conventionally colleges approach in a departmental and compartmental manner. In the existing curriculum patient benefit as a integrative component is missing. As a result, integration of different components the curriculum is a major lacuna in Indian curriculum.

The structure and duration of the program including the number of academic credits awarded and the mix of required elective courses should be appropriate to the educational outcomes and competencies to be achieved by pharmacy graduates.

Practice experiences should be undertaken at approved sites under the supervision of appropriately qualified and experienced trainers, who serve as practitioner- educators. Responsibilities of students and the trainer providing practical experiences should be clearly defined and mutually agreed.

2.5   Recourses

2.5.1 Faculty, staff and trainer

The college should have a sufficient number of qualified and experienced staff to effectively deliver and evaluate the professional degree program. The number should be such that adequate time is provided for faculty development in the form of continued training , research and other scholarly activities , service , and other professional activity including interface with pharmaceutical industries and community practice. The full-time faculty and staff may be complimented by part-time and voluntary faculty and trainers on site. Adequate support should be provided to allow effective and efficient operation of the college. Acceptable ratio between Teachers and students can work out expected number. 1:20 is the ratio suggested by Indian regulators.

Members of the faculty and staff, individually and collectively, should be committed to the mission and goals of the college, and respect their colleagues and students. Members of the faculty should possess the required professional and academic experience, has latest knowledge and abilities in current educational philosophy and techniques, and be committed to the advancement of the profession and the pursuit of research and other scholarly activities. The college should support continuing education of the faculty and staff, as related to responsibilities in the program. The college should also implement appropriate policies and procedures for the faculty, so that right persons are selected, retained and promoted in a transparent and consistent manner.

The college should ensure that the faculty composition, including any external relationship offers necessary expertise in biomedical, pharmaceutical, social/behavioral /administrative, and clinical sciences to meet the education and research needs as defined by the mission of the college. Members of the faculty, regardless of their discipline, should have or develop a conceptual understanding of current and proposed trends in pharmaceutical production and distribution.

Members of the faculty should have the capability and continued commitment to be effective teachers. Effective teaching requires knowledge, effective communication skills, and the understanding of pedagogy, including construction and delivery of the curriculum, which is relevant to the current needs of the society in terms of employability. Members of the faculty should deploy educational technologies and techniques which support various modes of educational delivery. One thing needs to be overemphasized that there is no compromise with competence of teaching staff for the purpose of delivery of professional expertise.

Mere transmission of knowledge is not adequate for the faculty. They should also generate knowledge through research. Scholarship exhibited by teachers is very essential. It involves scholarship of teaching, as evident and demonstrated by productive research and other scholarly activities, such as contributions to the scientific, professional, and educational literature; and publication of books and review articles. The college should generate an environment which encourages the faculty to development and better transmission of knowledge through scholarship and effective interaction with students. The faculty should also be encouraged for active involvement in governance of the college by participation in various administrative committees, participation in professional and scientific bodies and community service.

The college should identify trainers with right attitude in the professional set up, either of community pharmacy or industrial production. They should have a desire to educate others and have an aptitude to facilitate learning and evaluate the achievement of required competencies.

2.5.2 Financial resources

With the help of management, the college should develop and maintain a broad base of financial support to ensure that it has adequate financial resources necessary to provide a stable environment in which the college and the program can develop and accomplish its mission and goals. It is important that the manpower employed in the college should have a sense of security and stability to put their efforts for development of the college. Within the policies of the University and the management, the college should have a measure of autonomy in its use and allocation of financial resources, and it should operate with a budget that is planned, developed, and managed in accordance with sound and accepted management practices. Wherever applicable, the University administrators responsible for Pharmacy program and the management should have a clear understanding of the resource needs of the professional degree program, such as the need of to support scholarship and research and the requirements of the library, educational resources and experiential education. It is only with adequate financial resources that the institution will be able to achieve its vision, mission and goals.

2.5.3 Physical facilities

The college should have adequate and appropriate physical facilities to achieve its mission and goals. Both Pharmacy Council of India (PCI) and All India Council for Technical Education (AICTE) have announced details of physical facilities to run a Diploma or Degree program respectively. It is necessary that the physical facilities should meet the legal standards as announced by the regulatory authorities. The physical facilities should be safe, well maintained, and adequately equipped. They should provide a desirable, comfortable, and safe environment for teaching and learning, and facilitate interaction among administration, faculty, and students. The facilities should include offices, lecture rooms, small class rooms in the form of tutorial rooms, facilities for individual and small group study for students, student activity areas, information communication technologies (with appropriate data security and recovery systems), and other equipments and instrumentation to support administration, teaching, research and other scholarly activities. Equipments should be up-to date and well maintained. Wherever colleges need animals in their professional course work or research, proper and adequate animal facilities be maintained as per legal requirements. Legal clearance from Committee for Promotion of Safety of Experimental Animals (CPCSEA) is necessary. Frequent meetings of CPCSEA should be conducted and recorded in presence of representative, appointed by the competent authority.

2.5.4   Facilities for practical experiences

Wherever pharmacy practice experiences are necessary in the curriculum, necessary facilities should be provided. M. Pharm. (Pharmacy Practice) and Pharm. D. are the relevant courses. It is necessary to advance collaboratively the patient care service at relevant sites i.e. Hospitals linked to Pharmacy institutions conducting the courses. The college should establish and implement criteria for selection of an adequate number and mix of practice facilities. The respective responsibilities, commitments, and expectations of the college and the practice site regarding the education and evaluation of students should be agreed and, ideally, formalized in a written agreement or contract. Such an agreement should also address student-related matters such as health and safety issues, professional conduct expectations, and liabilities. The management and professional staff at practice sites should be committed to and supportive of the education of pharmacy students. The sites should have access to learning and information resources and a practice environment that promotes and supports pharmacist and student interactions with patients and other healthcare professionals.

2.5.5   Library and learning/educational resources

The college should ensure access for all faculty, preceptors, and students to a library and other learning/educational resources that are sufficient to support the professional degree program and to provide foe research and other scholarly activities in accordance with the mission and goals of the college. The college should fully incorporate and use these resources in the teaching and learning processes. In this context it is advisable that the college should conduct organized programs to teach the faculty, preceptors, and students about effective and efficient use of the library and other learning/ educational resources. In order to consolidate further, students, preceptor, and faculty opinions should be sought and evaluate regarding the adequacy of and access to library and learning/ educational resources.

3. Process

3.1 Planning

The college should develop, implement, and regularly revise a strategic plan to facilitate the advancement and achievement of its mission and goals. The strategic plan should develop by including all stake holders. The plan should seek input and review from administrators, faculty, staff, external trainers if any, students and even alumni. The plan should be based on an examination of present and projected environmental, professional, and programme-related factors. It should assess strengths, weaknesses, opportunities, and threats (SWOT analysis) relevant to the college from time to time. It should include a review of the mission statement, goals, and values for the college. The plan should define measurable outcomes and the processes to assess them; establish achievable timelines; identify the resources which need to be allocated; designate responsibilities to the appropriate person or group; and establish mechanisms for ongoing monitoring and reporting of progress. Thus the plan should be accompanied by appropriate monitoring mechanism.

3.2 Enrollment Management

The number of students enrolled in the program should be managed in alignment with available physical, financial, faculty, staff, training site, trainer, student services and other administrative resources. The number of students should be commensurate with available resources.

3.3 Evaluation and assessment

The college should establish and implement an evaluation plan or ongoing comprehensive system of evaluation which assesses achievement of the mission, goals and objectives. The evaluation should measure the extent of the desired outcomes of the professional degree program. Similarly, the extent to which the desired outcomes of research and other scholarly activities, service, and pharmacy practice programmes are being achieved should be measured. Assessment and evaluation activities should involve both external and internal stake holders. On one hand it is necessary to asses and evaluate performance of internal regular students; on the other hand it is also necessary to evaluate the performance of graduates in practice for their professionalism, leadership and effectiveness as agents of change in the profession. The college should use the analysis of process and outcome measures for continuous development and improvement of the professional degree programme.

The evaluation plan should describe the process and outcome assessments which will be measured and evaluated. It should also indicate the frequency of action, the individual or group responsible for data collection, analysis, and dissemination. It should also indicate the person (s) who will be responsible to receive and be authorised to act on the findings; and the manner by which resultant changes will be implemented, evaluated, documented, and communicated. The changes may reflect revisions in the curriculum or modifications of policies and procedures. The assessments employed in the evaluation plan or system should include defined formative and summative measures. A formative assessment measure is taken before completion of the activity e.g. Completing first, second or third year programme. A summative assessment is taken at the conclusion of the activity e.g. award of B. Pharm / M. Pharm / Pharm. D degree. A summative assessment is usually linked with a set of defined competencies.

Academic policies and procedures

The college should produce and make available to students and prospective students following information: criteria, policies, and procedures for admissions to and progression in the professional degree program. The brochure prepared for admission should clearly state prior training, experience, knowledge, skills, or attitudes needed for admission to the programme. The brochure should also indicate academic expectation of the programme, and professional standards for graduation. The college should have the final responsibility for enrolment and selection of students, both qualitatively and quantitatively.

Incidentally credit policies for courses are not implemented in all universities. However based on rational procedures and defensible assessments, the college should produce and available to make regular and prospective students policies about credit transfer and course waivers. In the present context it is equivalent to establishing equivalence of a course from one university with the curriculum of another university. The college should produce and make available to students and prospective students about criteria, policies, and procedures for academic progression, academic probation, remediation, missed course work, dismissal, re-admission, rights to due process and appeal mechanisms.

The college should have a system for monitoring student performance based on formative assessment of learning outcomes. Such an arrangement provides for early detection of academic difficulty. Remedial measures can be taken on students to avoid losing track with them for the entire course. The college should provide student services like tutorial support, faculty advising and remediation programme for students experiencing academic difficulties.

As a component of its evaluation system, the college should regularly asses the criteria, policies and procedures for admission and progression to ensure selection of good students, who have the greatest potential for academic success in the professional degree programme, and the ability to achieve the professional competencies and enter practise in different cities.

Student services

Within the organizational structure, the college should have a person responsible for the coordination of student services. For such a person responsibilities include student recruitment, orientation, provision of program information, information about financial aid and provisions for loan, academic and career counseling, and access to health care services. The college should have ordered, accurate and secure systems of student record. It is further necessary that there should be an archive of information about all students so that even alumni can trace back to their records if necessary.

The college should produce and make available to regular students and prospective students about a complete and accurate description of the professional degree program, including any disclosures required by the agency responsible for quality assurance of the program; e.g. NBA expects that if a college has multiple programs and only one of them is accreditated by NBA then the brochures of the college should not provide accreditation to the entire college.

Students representation and input

The college should consider student perspectives and include student representation, wherever appropriate, on committees, in policy development bodies, and in assessment and evaluation activities. Such announcements provide a sense of involvement to the students in the activities of the college. This feelings in the minds of students, encourages willing participation in various activities of the college.

The college should have a student representation/ governance structure as well as suitable committees of students to develop leadership and professionalism, to ensure a forum for student dialogue and to ensure adequate communication of student opinions and perspectives. Through these activities, students should develop a feeling that the administration, faculty, staff along with students are working for a cohesive cause of participating in a professional activity.

Instruments and techniques, such as course evaluations, focus groups, meetings with the program director or other administrative leaders, and exit interviews should be systematically employed to obtain student perspectives on faculty, curriculum, student services, and other aspects of the professional degree program. It is necessary that feedback from students should be taken seriously in order to improve functioning of the college. The assessment data obtained from the students should be systematically analyzed, nterpreted and used to improve all aspects of the program. It is good to be transparent on this issue. Thus the college should share with students the aggregate results and outcomes of their participation in program evaluation and improvement.

3.7 Curricular development and improvement

The faculty of the college should be collectively responsible for the development, organization, delivery, review, and improvement of the curriculum. The curriculum must define the expected educational outcomes and competencies. In fact, curriculum should be developed based entirely on defined competencies. The curriculum should be developed with attention to sequencing, reinforcement, integration and application of content, and the selection of appropriate teaching and learning methods and assessments. Instructions should be coordinated across the college/ departments and faculty disciplines to ensure appropriate coverage of all curricular areas and avoid unnecessary redundance and overlap of topics e.g. content in medicinal chemistry regarding mechanism of action of drugs can be coordinated with teaching in pharmacology. The curriculum should include tidactic course work, opportunities for small group work to promote Problem Based Learning (PBL), laboratories, simulations of industry setup or animal demonstrations, and supervised educational experiences in actual field work. All courses and elements of the curriculum should be mapped or linked to the expected competencies and educational outcomes.

Ideally the curriculum should incorporate both mandatory and elective courses. Elective courses may be selected by the student based on their personal interest and societal needs. The college may offer several electives based on the need and expertise of the faculty. The standard should specify the minimum number of academic years, hours or credits for the professional degree program. Ongoing development, review and continuous improvement of the curriculum should be guided by assessment data and be sensible to changing state of knowledge in healthcare or new technologies and the needs and demands emerging from health systems, including expectations of consumers. Every professional program succeeds based on satisfying changing needs of the consumer. Further every professional program succeeds based on the fact that it satisfies real professional needs of the society. Curricular revision should include new content without altering duration of the program. The revision needs to ensure overall integrity of the curriculum, avoiding curricular overload, dilution of focus and insufficient depth of coverage for essential components of the curriculum.

3.8 Teaching and learning methodologies

Different educational methodologies are required to support the achievement of the different competencies required for practice of pharmacy. The competency includes knowledge, skills, attitudes, behaviors, judgments and values. Throughout the curriculum the college should use and integrate teaching and learning methods which have been shown to train the graduates through competencies. This has to be achieved through curricular assessments and other related studies. Faculty should employ active learning strategies and encourage students to ask questions wherever possible. The present classroom teaching is a passive learning method with minimal student involvement. Unless students get convinced about need of the learning as related to problems on field, the real process of teaching-learning is not much effective. Students should be encouraged and assisted to assume responsibility of their own learning and to participate in the education of others. By and large, teaching and learning methods should support achievements of the stated outcomes and competencies, promote the development and maturation of critical thinking and problem-solving skills, meet the diverse learning of students and enable students to transform from teacher dependant to active, self directed, lifelong learners. Once students become self and lifelong learners, professional advancements is automatically ensured. The main purpose of the college is to create an environment of self and lifelong learning. Ideally the college should have access to educational experts from the institution or from other institutions for the development of staff. Wherever applicable colleges should have the policy of using external educational expertise to develop teaching and learning methods.

3.9 Student assessment methodologies

Assessment methodologies and criteria should be well defined. These should be documented and evaluated against the educational outcomes which are aimed at. Assessment data can be used for curricular improvement to examine how the assessment methods promote learning and could be further developed to improve the alignment with educational outcomes. The link between needed professional competencies and curricular content should be processed through assessment methodologies.

3.10 Faculty, staff and preceptor development and evaluation

The college has to provide support for an effective continuing professional program for full time, part time and voluntary faculty, external trainers and staff consistent with their responsibilities in the professional degree program. The college should review the performance of faculty, staff and external trainers on a regular basis. Criteria for performance review should be commensurate with responsibilities in the professional degree program.

The faculty and staff evaluation process should be annual, involve self assessment, and include appropriate input from piers, supervisors and students. Involvement of alumni in the professional growth of existing students is a vital factor for the success of activities of the college.

APPENDIX

List of documents/records to be made available during the visit (a tentative list)

(Instruction: Records of last three years to be made available, wherever applicable)

The following list is just a guideline. The institution may prepare its own list of documents in support of the SAR that it is submitting. The soft copy of these documents (in the form of statements and list only) may be appended with the SAR.

INSTITUTE SPECIFIC

I.1 Land papers, built-plan, and approval, etc.

I.2 Composition of governing, senate, and other academic and administrative bodies; their functions; and responsibilities. List of all the meetings held in the past three years along with the attendance records. Representative minutes and action taken reports of a few meetings of such bodies along with the list of current faculty members who are members of such bodies.

I.3 Rules, policies, and procedures published by the institution including service book and academic regulations and others, along with the proof that the employees/students are aware of the rules and procedures.

I.4 Budget allocation and utilisation, audited statement of accounts.

I.5 Informative website.

I.6 Library resources---books and journal holdings.

I.7 Listing of core, computing, and manufacturing, etc., labs.

I.8 Records of T&P and career and guidance cells.

I.9 Records of safety checks and critical installations.

I.10 Medical care records and usages of ambulance, etc.

I.11 Academic calendar, schedule of tutorial, and makeup classes.

I.12 Handouts/files along with outcomes, list of additional topics to meet the outcomes.

I.13 Set of question papers, assignments, evaluation schemes, etc.

I.14 Feedback form, analysis of feedback, and corrective actions.

I.15 Documented feedback received from the stakeholders (e.g., industries, parents, alumni, financiers, etc.) of the institution.

I.16 List of faculty who teach first year courses along with their qualifications.

I.17 Results of the first year students.

PROGRAM SPECIFIC

Each programme for which an institution seeks accreditation or reaccreditation must have in place the following:

P.1 NBA accreditation reports of the past visits, if any

P.2 Department budget and allocations (past three years data)

P.3 Admission---seats filled and ranks (last three years data)

P.4 List/number of students who h a v e cleared the programme in four years (last three years data)

P.5 CGPA (last three years data of students' CGPA/ percentage)

P.6 Placement and higher studies (last three years data)

P.7 Professional society activities, events, conferences organised, etc.

P.8 List of students' papers along with hard copies of the publications; professional society publications/magazines, etc.

P.9 Sample best and average project reports/thesis

P.10 Details of student-faculty ratio

P.11 Faculty details with their service books, salary details, sample appointment letters, promotion and award letters/certificates

P.12 Faculty list with designation, qualification, joining date, publication, R&D, interaction details

P.13 List of faculty publications along with DOIs and publication/citation details

P.14 List of R&D and consultancy projects along with approvals and project completion reports

P.15 List and proofs of faculty interaction with outside world

P.16 List of classrooms, faculty rooms

P.17 List of programme- specific laboratories and computing facility within department.

P.18 List of non-teaching staff with their appointment letters, etc.

P.19 List of short-term courses, workshops arranged, and course modules developed

P.20 Records of new programme- specific facility created, if any

P.21 Records of overall programme- specific improvements, if any

P.22 Curriculum, POs, PEOs, Mission, and Vision statements

P.23 Correlation of outcomes with the PEOs

P.24 Correlation of course outcomes with the POs

P.25 Course files, plan of course delivery, question papers, answer scripts, assignments, reports of assignments, project reports, report of design projects, list of laboratory experiments, reports of laboratory experiments, etc.

P.26 Rubrics developed to validate the POs

P.27 Continuous improvement in the PEOs

P.28 Improvement in curriculum for correlating the POs and t h e PEOs

P.29 Direct and indirect assessment methods to show attainment of the POs

P.30 Stakeholder's involvement in the process of improvement of the PEOs and t h e POs

P.31 Collected forms of various indirect assessment tools (e.g. alumni survey, employer survey)

P.32 Any other document which may be necessary to evaluate the SAR.

Competencies of Pharmacists suggested by USA, AUSTRALIA, FIP and UK

➢ USA

I. Clinical problem solving, judgment, and decision making

A. Monitor patients in the health care setting.

1. Collect patient-specific data to identify problems and individualize care.
2. Perform relevant physical assessment.
3. Interview patient, family, and other health care professionals to complement patient's medical history, medication therapy history, and review of systems.
4. Identify additional data needed.
5. Identify patient specific goals of therapy.
6. Prospectively develop a plan for ongoing evaluation of progression of disease, development of disease related complications, efficacy of drug therapy, and development of drug-related adverse effects.

B. Assess patient-specific medical problems.

1. Organize, interpret, and analyze patient-specific data.
2. Synthesize patient data to form an assessment.
3. Develop a comprehensive medical problem list.
4. Assess the status, etiology, risk factors, and complications of the patient's medical problems.
5. Prioritize medical problems based on urgency and severity.

6. Identify preventive and health maintenance issues.

7. Persuasively communicate a justification for one's assessment.

C. Evaluate patient-specific drug therapy and therapeutic problems.

1. Evaluate the appropriateness of drug therapy, including the choice of drug, and the dose, route, frequency, and duration of therapy.

2. Evaluate the efficacy of current drug therapy.

3. Identify potential or actual drug-induced adverse effects.

4. Identify potential or actual drug interactions.

5. Identify contraindications to therapy.

6. Identify untreated problems.

7. Assess patient compliance and factors that may influence compliance.

D. Design a comprehensive drug therapy plan for patient specific problems.

1. Select nonpharmacologic therapeutic measures.

2. Select optimal drug, dose, route, frequency, and duration of therapy.

3. Select strategies for prevention of disease.

4. Incorporate the significance of potential drug interactions and adverse effects into the recommended plan.

5. Persuasively justify recommendations based on patient-specific pharmacologic, pharmacokinetic, pharmacodynamic, pharmacogenomic, pharmacoeconomic, ethical, legal, and evidence based information.

E. Collaborate with patients, caregivers, and other health care professionals.

1. Take responsibility for patient care duties.

2. Reliably complete tasks and assignments.

3. Manage time appropriately to be well prepared for clinical activities.

II. Communication and education

A. Educate patients.

1. Identify appropriate patient educational needs.

2. Recognize patient education barriers.

3. Use appropriate educational methods to educate patients regarding drug therapy.

4. Use language appropriate for the patient.

5. Assess patient's level of knowledge and skill acquisition.

B. Educate other health care professionals.

1. Identify the educational needs of health care professionals.

2. Establish rapport with other health care professionals.

    3. Communicate recommendations or relevant information to health care professionals in a manner appropriate to their training, skills, and needs.

    4. Provide background information and primary literature to health care professionals as needed.

C. Communicate effectively.

    1. Effectively communicate at a level appropriate tothe audience.

    2. Interpret verbal and nonverbal cues.

    3. Use specific, clear, and appropriate terminology.

    4. Maintain appropriate eye contact.

    5. Communicate in an organized, logical, and concise manner.

    6. Display an appropriate level of confidence.

    7. Demonstrate tact.

    8. Answer questions clearly and completely.

D. Document interventions in the patient medical record.

    1. Clearly document drug therapy reconciliation and other patient-related interventions.

    2. Effectively communicate assessment, including supporting subjective and objective data.

    3. Effectively communicate the therapeutic plan.

III. Medical information evaluation and management

A. Demonstrate the motivation and commitment to become a lifelong learner.

    1. Effectively self-assess knowledge and limitations.

    2. Define the question to be answered or problem to be solved.

    3. Demonstrate habits of self-learning.

B. Retrieve biomedical literature using appropriate search strategies.

C. Interpret biomedical literature with regard to study design, methodology, statistical analysis, significance of reported data, and conclusions.

D. Integrate data obtained from multiple sources to derive an overall conclusion or answer.

IV. Management of patient populations

A. Patient safety and drug therapy evaluation

    1. Collect data to characterize or identify health system–related problems in providing optimal health care.

    2. Interpret data to characterize health system–related problems.

    3. Design a plan to improve the delivery and quality of pharmacotherapy.

4. Develop a justification for and garner support for implementation of the plan.

5. Design measures to monitor the success of the plan during and following implementation.

6. Collaborate to implement the plan.

7. Monitor the plan and implement appropriate modifications.

8. Educate appropriate audiences on results of health system-related pharmacotherapy problem assessment and recommended solutions.

B. Critical pathways

1. Identify diagnoses, procedures, or drugs that involve high risk, high patient volume, high process variability, and/or high cost.

2. Select a multidisciplinary health care team based on likelihood of involvement in the pathway.

3. Identify appropriate outcome measures based on review of the current medical literature and assessment of current processes.

4. Document processes and outcomes for current practice and compare with current literature-based standards (benchmarking).

5. Elucidate discrepancies between current literature based standards and current practice.

6. Develop the pathway with clearly defined goals and outcomes, patient education criteria, patient safety documentation, and monitoring.

V. Therapeutic knowledge areas

A. Apply disease-oriented knowledge of the following areas.

1. Anatomy, physiology, and pathophysiology

2. Epidemiology, etiology, risk factors, and signs and symptoms

3. Natural course and prognosis

4. Laboratory and diagnostic test interpretation

B. Demonstrate competence in the pharmacotherapy of the following medical problems.

1. Bone and joint

   a. Degenerative joint disease

   b. Osteoporosis

   c. Gout

2. Cardiovascular

   a. Hypertension

   b. Heart failure

   c. Coronary artery disease

    d.   Acute coronary syndromes

    e.   Atrial fibrillation

    f.   Thromboembolic disorders

    g.   Dyslipidemias

    h.   Cardiopulmonary resuscitation

    i.   Peripheral arterial disease

    j.   Shock (hypovolemic, cardiogenic, and septic)

    k.   Stroke

3.   Dermatologic

    a.   Acne

    b.   Urticaria

    c.   Psoriasis

    d.   Eczema

4.   Endocrine

    a.   Diabetes mellitus

    b.   Hypothyroidism, hyperthyroidism

    c.   Adrenal disorders

    d.   Hormonal contraception

5.   Gastrointestinal

    a.   Gastroesophageal reflux disease

    b.   Nausea and vomiting

    c.   Stress ulcer disease

    d.   Peptic ulcer disease

    e.   Upper gastrointestinal haemorrhage

    f.   Hepatitis

    g.   Cirrhosis

    h.   Pancreatitis

    i.   Inflammatory bowel disease

    j.   Cholelithiasis

    k.   Diarrhea and constipation

6.   Genitourinary

    a.   Prostate hypertrophy

    b.   Urinary incontinence

7. Hematologic
   a. Anemias
   b. Clotting factor deficiencies
   c. Sickle cell disease
   d. Disseminated intravascular coagulopathy
   e. Thrombocytopenias

8. Immunologic
   a. Hypersensitivity reactions
   b. Allergic rhinitis
   c. Organ transplantation
   d. Human immunodeficiency syndrome

9. Infectious diseases
   a. Meningitis
   b. Endocarditis
   c. Fungal infections
   d. Gastrointestinal infection
   e. Intraabdominal infection
   f. Opportunistic infection
   g. Osteomyelitis
   h. Otitis media
   i. Peritonitis
   j. Pneumonia
   k. Prostatitis
   l. Septic arthritis
   m. Sexually transmitted diseases
   n. Sinusitis
   o. Skin and soft tissue infections
   p. Surgical prophylaxis
   q. Tuberculosis
   r. Upper respiratory tract infections
   s. Urinary tract infections
   t. Viral infections

10. Neurologic
    a. Epilepsy, status epilepticus

    b. Pain management

    c. Stroke

    d. Headache, migraine

    e. Peripheral neuropathy

    f. Parkinson's disease

    g. Dementia

    h. Delirium

11. Oncologic

    a. Melanoma

    b. Breast cancer

    c. Colorectal cancer

    d. Leukemia

    e. Lung cancer

    f. Lymphoma

    g. Prostate cancer

12. Psychiatric

    a. Drug and alcohol abuse

    b. Anxiety disorders

    c. Attention-deficit–hyperactivity disorder

    d. Depressive disorders

    e. Schizophrenia

    f. Bipolar disorders

13. Pulmonary

    a. Asthma

    b. Chronic obstructive pulmonary disease

    c. Respiratory distress syndrome

    d. Respiratory failure

    e. Cystic fibrosis

    f. Pulmonary hypertension

14. Renal

    a. Acute renal failure

    b. Chronic renal failure

    c. Renal replacement therapies (hemodialysis, peritoneal dialysis, continuous renal replacement)

    d. Nephrolithiasis

    e. Glomerulonephritis

    f. Fluid and electrolyte disorders

15. Rheumatologic

    a. Polymyositis

    b. Scleroderma

    c. Systemic lupus erythematosus

    d. Sarcoidosis

    e. Rheumatoid arthritis

C. Apply the following principles in the setting of each disease state, patient population, and/or therapeutic category.

    1.   Pharmacokinetics

    2.   Pharmacodynamics

    3.   Pharmacoeconomics

    4.   Pharmacogenomics

    5.   Toxicology

    6.   Empiric antibiotic therapy

    7.   Health screening

    8.   Health maintenance

    9.   Drug interactions (drug-disease, drug-drug, drug laboratory, drug-nutrient)

    10. Nondrug therapies and nonprescription remedies

    11. Herbal products

    12. Immunizations

    13. Geriatric considerations

    14. Pediatric considerations

    15. Nutrition (enteral and parenteral)

    16. Fluids, electrolytes, acid-base balance

➢ AUSTRALIA

In Australia the competencies have been identified under 8 domains and each of the domains has been further identified with certain standards. The details of domains and standards are indicated below.

Domain 1. Professional and ethical practice

Domain 2. Communication, collaboraton and self management

Domain 3. Leadership and management

Domain 4. Review and supply prescribed medicines

Domain 5. Prepare pharmaceutical products

Domain 6. Deliver primary and preventive care

Domain 7. Promote and contribute to optimal use of medicines

Domain 8. Critcal analysis, research and education

Domain 1. Professional and ethical practice

- Standard 1.1 Practise legally
- Standard 1.2 Practise to accepted standards
- Standard 1.3 Deliver 'patient-centred' care
- Standard 1.4 Manage quality and safety
- Standard 1.5 Maintain and extend professional competence

Domain 2. Communication, collaboration and self-management

- Standard 2.1 Communicate effectively
- Standard 2.2 Work to resolve problems
- Standard 2.3 Collaborate with members of the health care team
- Standard 2.4 Manage conflict
- Standard 2.5 Commitment to work and the workplace
- Standard 2.6 Plan and manage professional contribution
- Standard 2.7 Supervise personnel

Domain 3. Leadership and Management

- Standard 3.1 Provide leadership and organisational planning
- Standard 3.2 Manage and develop personnel
- Standard 3.3 Manage pharmacy infrastructure and resources
- Standard 3.4 Manage quality service delivery
- Standard 3.5 Provide a safe and secure work environment

Domain 4. Review and supply prescribed medicines

- Standard 4.1 Undertake initial prescription assessment
- Standard 4.2 Consider the appropriateness of prescribed medicines
- Standard 4.3 Dispense prescribed medicines

Domain 5. Prepare pharmaceutical products

- Standard 5.1 Consider product requirements
- Standard 5.2 Prepare non-sterile drug products
- Standard 5.3 Aseptically prepare sterile drug products
- Standard 5.4 Prepare cytotoxic drug products

Domain 6. Deliver Primary and Preventive Health care

- Standard 6.1 Assess primary health care needs
- Standard 6.2 Deliver primary health care
- Standard 6.3 Contribute to public and preventive health

Domain 7. Promote and contribute to optimal use of medicines

- Standard 7.1 Contribute to therapeutic decision-making
- Standard 7.2 Provide ongoing medication management
- Standard 7.3 Influence patterns of medicine use

Domain 8. Critical analysis, research and education

- Standard 8.1 Retrieve, analyse and synthesise information
- Standard 8.2 Engage in health, medicines or pharmacy practice research
- Standard 8.3 Formally educate and train students and healthcare colleagues

➢ FIP

FIP has identified the competencies under two major areas and four main focus areas. The details are as follows

The two major areas are:

1. Scientific knowledge
2. Management knowledge

The scientific knowledge is further divided in two focus areas: Patient focus and population focus; while

The management knowledge is divided in two focus areas: Practice focus and system focus.

Every focus area is identified with a set of competencies:

The patient focus has following main and related competencies:

PHARMACEUTICAL CARE:

Patient care and diagnosis

Assessment of medicines

1.3   Compounding medicines

1.4   Dispensing medicines

1.5   Monitor medicines

The population focus has following main and related competencies :

2.   PHARMACEUTICAL PUBLIC HEALTH :

2.1   Health promotion

Medicines information and advice

The practice focus has following main and related competencies :

3.   PROFESSIONAL/PERSONAL

3.1   Communication skills

3.2   Continuous professional development

3.3   Legal and regulatory practice

3.4   Professional and ethical practice

3.5   Quality assurance and research in the workplace

3.6   Self-management

The system focus has following main and related competencies

4.   ORGANIZATION AND MANAGEMENT

4.1   Budget and reimbursement.

4.2   Human resource management

4.3   Improvement of services

4.4   Procurement of drugs

4.5   Supply chain and management

4.6   Workplace management

➤ UK

The comptencies identified in UK are subdivided in 3 parts.

1. Competencies for Industrial pharmacists

2. Competencies for practicing pharmacist as identified by pharmaceutical society of Great Britain

3. Detailed competencies for general, community, hospital pharmacists and p⋅ registration tutors.

1. Competencies for Industrial pharmacists

In UK, a study guide for pinpointing competencies needed by qualified p⋅ pharmaceutical industries is prepared to identify their knowledge and⋅ experiences. The document is partially reproduced here. Similar document ⋅

conditions citing relevant Indian requirements as per the relevant laws is desirable. The document will be very useful for training Industrial pharmacists. Curriculum based on such a document will be very much relevant to Indian pharmacists.

Guide to the Knowledge and Practical Experience Required by Qualified Persons in the Pharmaceutical Industry

Study Guide

1.0   The Qualified Person in the Pharmaceutical Industry: Background

2.0   The three foundation knowledge elements:

 a Pharmaceutical law and administration

 b The role and professional duties of a Qualified Person

 c Quality management systems

3.0   Additional knowledge requirements for the Qualified Person:

 d Mathematics and statistics

 e Medicinal chemistry and therapeutics

 f Pharmaceutical formulation and processing

 g Pharmaceutical microbiology

 h Analysis and testing

 i Pharmaceutical packaging

 j Active pharmaceutical ingredients

 k Investigational medicinal products

4.0   The Qualified Person: practical experience requirements

 4.1 Illustration of requirements

5.0   Role of the Qualified Person

 5.1 Functions of the Qualified Person under Directives 2001/83/EC and 2001/82/EC

 5.2 Functions of the Qualified Person under Directive 2001/20/EC

6.0   Summary

1.0 The Qualified Person in the Pharmaceutical Industry: Background

The Medicines and Healthcare products Regulatory Agency (MHRA) of the UK Department of Health, and the Veterinary Medicines Directorate (VMD), have interpreted the requirements of the Pharmaceutical Directive 2001/83/EC and the Veterinary Directive 2001/82/EC through a Study Guide, drawn up by a panel of experts, and have given authority to three professional bodies, the Society of Biology, the Royal Pharmaceutical Society and the Royal Society of Chemistry, to operate an assessment procedure for their members. The assessments seek to determine an applicant's suitability for being named on company Manufacturer's Licence.

The professional bodies' role is to certify the eligibility of the applicant for nomination as a Qualified Person on a Manufacturer's Licence. The applicant must be able to demonstrate that he or she can satisfy the knowledge and experience requirements of Articles 49 and 50 of the "Pharmaceutical Directive" 2001/83/EC (amended by Directive 2004/27/EC), Articles 53 and 54 of the "Veterinary Directive" 2001/82/EC (amended by 2004/28/EC), or Article 13 of the "Clinical Trials Directive" 2001/20/EC. Acceptance of a person, certified as eligible for nomination, on a Manufacturer's Licence is a matter for the Licensing Authority.

The certification process includes submission of a completed application form, the sponsorship of an applicant by a Qualified Person who is also a member of the Society of Biology, the Royal Pharmaceutical Society or the Royal Society of Chemistry, the payment of an application fee, and for applications under the permanent provisions, an oral assessment of the applicant's knowledge and experience.

Applications under the transitional provisions of Article 50 of 2001/83/EC do not normally involve an oral assessment. Since the change in veterinary legislation in 2005, applications can no longer be made under the transitional provisions of 2001/82/EC. The VMD has the capacity to appoint QPs independently of the Tripartite bodies.

Since 1992 the oral assessments have been conducted jointly by the three professional bodies.

The oral assessment is carried out by a panel of assessors drawn from all three professional bodies, who are themselves well-acquainted with the role of a Qualified Person. The three professional bodies have agreed with the MHRA and VMD that, in principle, an individual who has been certified as eligible for nomination as a Qualified Person is also potentially eligible for transfer from one Manufacturer's Licence to another, although the final decision for accepting a person as a Qualified Person on a licence rests with the Licensing Authority in the UK. In consequence the assessors must be satisfied that an applicant, after a suitable induction period, will be able to function as a Qualified Person in any licensed undertaking.

Appeals can be made by applicants to their professional body as appropriate.

A guide to the body of knowledge required by the Qualified Person is set out in the following pages. This document should be studied in conjunction with the current edition of the Medicines and Healthcare products Regulatory Agency's (MHRA) "Rules and Guidance for Pharmaceutical Manufacturers and Distributors (known as "the Orange Guide").

The Joint Professional Bodies no longer issue a "Sources of Reference" document. Frequent legislation changes result in the document rapidly becoming out-of-date. Applicants are reminded that a thorough understanding of current legislation is required meet the requirements of this Study Guide.

2.0 The three foundation knowledge elements

a. Pharmaceutical law and administration

To assure patient safety the manufacture and distribution of pharmaceutical products is highly regulated within the European Union. The Qualified Person, in particular, must ensure that all legislative obligations are fully satisfied before any product is released for sale.

A Qualified Person must have a comprehensive knowledge of all European and National legislation relating to the manufacture, storage and supply of licensed medicinal products and the interpretation of the law as exemplified in the current edition of the MHRA's "Rules and Guidance for Pharmaceutical Manufacturers and Distributors ", ("the Orange Guide").

Applicants will be expected to demonstrate a thorough understanding of the following:

- European pharmaceutical directives (including but not limited to 2001/83/EC,
- 2001/82/EC, 2001/20/EC, 2003/94/EC, 2004/24/EC, 2004/27/EC, 2004/28/EC);
- the UK Medicines Act (1968) and other UK national medicines legislation, and the

  Veterinary Medicines Regulation, including amendments;
- Marketing, Manufacturing and Wholesaler Authorisation requirements and responsibilities; the role, legal status and structure of both the European and British Pharmacopoeias,including the Certification procedure of the EDQM;
- the organisation of the UK MHRA, the role of the European Agency for the Evaluation of Medicinal Products (EMEA), and the role of the Veterinary Medicines Directorate (VMD); procedures for dealing with complaints and product recalls and the role of the MHRA's
- Defective Medicines Reporting Centre, CHMP and CVMP guidelines on quality;
- The International Conference on Harmonisation (ICH and VICH) guidelines;
- Mutual Recognition Agreements (MRAs);
- Pharmaceutical Inspection Co-operation Scheme (PICS);

b. The role and professional duties of a Qualified Person

It is incumbent upon all Qualified Persons, whether or not members of one of the three professional bodies, that they discharge their professional duties in accordance with the Code of Practice for Qualified Persons, which the three professional bodies (SB, RPS and RSC), in collaboration with the MHRA and VMD, have produced.

It is the responsibility of the Qualified Person to certify that a product has been manufactured in accordance with its Marketing Authorisation, and with Good Manufacturing Practice (GMP).

The Qualified Person might not have direct line responsibility for many of the activities which could affect compliance with GMP or the Marketing Authorisation. However, they must be aware of any incidents or deviations which may influence their decision to release a batch for sale.

Applicants will be expected to demonstrate a thorough understanding of the following:

- batch review and decision making on disposition.
- the principles and practice of current GMP and QA as given in European Directives and
- Guides on Good Manufacturing Practice including relevant Regulations made under the
- Medicines Act 1968 and the current edition of the MHRA's Rules and Guidance for
- Pharmaceutical Manufacturers and Distributors, ("the Orange Guide");
- the conduct and obligations of MA and MAA holders;
- the preparation for and management of Regulatory Inspections.

c. Quality management systems

The manufacture of pharmaceutical products requires the establishment and implementation of an effective 'quality management system' (QMS). The concepts of QA, GMP and Quality Control (QC), which are inter-related, form the basis of such a system for the manufacture of pharmaceutical products.

Applicants will be expected to demonstrate a thorough understanding of the following:

- the philosophy and basic principles of QA;
- the design criteria for an effective QMS;
- auditing and self inspections;
- deviations and change control;
- documentation and record keeping;
- the interpersonal skills (leadership, delegation, communication, etc) necessary to implement an effective QMS;
- the concepts associated with risk management;
- the principles of design, selection, qualification and maintenance of premises, equipment, utilities, and services;
- calibration, preventative maintenance and training;
- the principles of purchasing and supplier certification, including knowledge of supply
- chains and material control and the roles of brokers, distributors and repackagers;

- production planning, scheduling, and inventory control;
- annual product quality reviews;
- the interface between QA and the Development, Regulatory Affairs, and Marketing Departments;
- the skills and competences needed to provide effective Good Pharmaceutical
- Manufacturing Practice training;
- organisational structures and reporting relationships;
- technical agreements and auditing in contract giving and acceptance.

3.0 Additional knowledge requirements for the Qualified Person
d Mathematics and statistics

The practical application of basic statistical tools in pharmaceutical production and QA is essential in demonstrating the capability of processes or the acceptability of materials.

Applicants will be expected to demonstrate an understanding of the following:

- Statistical Process Control;
- BS6000-6001 (Sampling plans);
- Process Control Charts;
- Acceptable Quality Levels (AQLs) (subset of 6001/2);
- statistics applied during analytical method validation.

e. Medicinal chemistry and therapeutics

The Qualified Person must have an understanding of the actions and uses of medicines in clinical practice in order to judge their significance for the manufacture of sales material or clinical trial supplies. Evaluating the significance of cross-contamination hazards or product complaints are examples where such knowledge is important.

Applicants will be expected to demonstrate an understanding of the following:

- basic physiology;
- outline knowledge of the autonomic nervous system and some general aspects of chemical structure/pharmacological action relationships;
- summary of key therapeutic drug classifications with examples;
- examples of disease states and their treatment with medicinal products;
- general absorption, distribution, metabolism and excretion of drugs;
- principal routes of drug administration;
- role of the company medical department;
- pharmacovigilance related to quality monitoring;
- general implications of clinical knowledge of drugs upon facility design, plant segregation/isolation, cleaning verification and production scheduling.

f. Pharmaceutical formulation and processing

The formulation and processing conditions employed in the manufacture of medicinal products have a significant effect upon their safety, quality and efficacy. Even subtle changes to the input materials and/or processing conditions can have a profound adverse effect on content uniformity, stability, bioavailability, and other attributes which are not detectable by routine QC testing.

It is vitally important that the Qualified Person understands the principles of formulation and pharmaceutical processing to ensure that informed release decisions are made.

Applicants will be expected to demonstrate an understanding of the following:

- the major processing techniques, their limitations and critical control parameters;
- the factors that could potentially affect content uniformity, stability (chemical, physical and microbiological) and bioavailability in manufacture;
- the principles of process validation and control;
- the principles of technology transfer and production scale-up;
- pre-formulation studies and product development;
- the storage and distribution of materials and finished products.

g. Pharmaceutical microbiology

The Qualified Person must understand the significance of the presence of bacteria, yeasts, moulds, viruses and toxins in pharmaceutical raw materials, products and production environments. In addition, they must understand how to prevent contamination by good product design, GMP and control over starting materials, intermediates, finished products, production plant and processes, people and the environment.

Applicants will be expected to demonstrate an understanding of the following:

- sources and types of micro-organisms as related to pharmaceutical production;
- production of sterile and non-sterile products and associated environmental controls;
- bacterial endotoxins and pyrogens, their sources, removal and testing;
- microbiology of water, its production and distribution systems;
- sterilisation and disinfection methods;
- interpretation of microbiological data;
- validation of microbiological test methods;
- microbiological specifications;
- selection and use of preservatives;
- microbiological test methods used in routine manufacture and product development;
- rapid methods of microbiological testing.

h. Analysis and testing

The sampling and testing of materials does not by itself assure product quality. It must be seen as one part of a comprehensive 'Quality management system', including QA and GMP, which must be correctly implemented and controlled.

The data generated by laboratory testing of samples must be evaluated before materials are released for sale.

Applicants will be expected to demonstrate an understanding of the following:

GCLP (Good Control Laboratory Practice);

- quality control of sterile and non-sterile dosage forms;
- interpretation of analytical data and non-conforming results;
- the principal qualitative and quantitative analytical methods in common use;
- analytical chemistry as relevant to the properties of medicinal products and materials;
- the principles of method selection and validation;
- the design of sampling regimes;
- biological test methods and interpretation of results;
- physical and organoleptic testing;
- stability testing (protocols & methods);
- the significance of degradation, contamination and adulteration of pharmaceutical materials;
- the types, purpose, significance and management of systems of in-process control;
- the International Conference on Harmonisation (ICH) guidelines for method validation, impurities and stability testing;

i. Pharmaceutical packaging

It is a requirement of GMP that holders of Manufacturing Authorisations establish procedures for their packaging operations to minimise the risk of cross-contamination, mix-up or substitutions. The Qualified Person must understand the importance of controlling packaging components (both primary and printed materials) throughout the supply chain to assure the quality of finished products.

Applicants will be expected to demonstrate an understanding of the following:

- control of packaging components by suppliers and throughout production;
- the chain of systems which ensure the integrity and accuracy of textual information from originator to routine production; the layout and organisation of packaging operations;
- causes of label and other printed component mix-ups;
- packaging and labelling processes and equipment;

- the testing of packaging materials including pack integrity testing;
- product security (automated systems, reconciliation, line clearance etc);
- in-process controls;
- effects of packaging materials on product stability;
- selection of packaging materials;
- tamper-evidence and anti-counterfeiting measures.

j. Active pharmaceutical ingredients

The Qualified Person must understand the influence of manufacturing pathways and associated physical and physico-chemical attributes, of both active pharmaceutical ingredients and major excipients, on the quality of the finished dosage form.

Applicants will be expected to demonstrate an understanding of the following:

- the steps commonly taken in the manufacture of active pharmaceutical ingredients and excipients (including biopharmaceuticals), their purpose and limitations;
- the generation of impurities, their identification, quantification, and elimination;
- the physico-chemical and biological properties of active pharmaceutical ingredients, and excipients, and their effect on the attributes of the final dosage form;
- the specific requirements for bulk materials intended for sterile products;
- the nature of controls for the manufacture of bulk biological and biotech products;
- auditing of API manufacturers.

k. Investigational medicinal products

The manufacture, packaging and distribution of investigational medicinal products must be controlled. There are significant differences between the manufacture of IMPs and licensed dosage forms. The Qualified Person must understand these differences together with the safeguards required to assure the quality of IMP supply.

Applicants will be expected to demonstrate an understanding of the following:

- specific GMPs associated with the manufacture of investigational medicinal products;
- the control of active and placebo forms;
- the control of packaging operations and blinding;
- the control and release of imported IMPs;
- the control and release of comparators;
- effective batch documentation, sampling and batch release;
- change control and material traceability;
- controls surrounding the procurement of Clinical Trial (CT) supplies;
- the principles of clinical trial design and Good Clinical Practice (GCP).

4.0 The Qualified Person: practical experience requirements

The precise wording used in Article 49 of the Pharmaceutical Directive 2001/83/EC is as follows:

"The qualified person shall have acquired practical experience over at least two years, in one or more undertakings which are authorised to manufacture medicinal products, in the activities of qualitative analysis of medicinal products, of quantitative analysis of active substances and of the testing and checking necessary to ensure the quality of medicinal products".

The three professional bodies have interpreted this legal obligation as requiring the applicant to have had at least #one or two years of relevant practical experience in assuring the quality of medicinal products during their manufacture, including Good Manufacturing Practice, as defined in the current edition of the MHRA's 'Rules and Guidance for Pharmaceutical Manufacturers and Distributors ("the Orange Guide"). (#In the UK, the MHRA and VMD have approved one year of practical experience for pharmacists).

4.1 Illustration of requirements

1. The applicant must have had at least #one/two years relevant practical experience in one or more of those activities embraced by the term QA (as defined and detailed in the EC Good Manufacturing Practice Guide, and the EC Directive 2001/83/EC) gained in premises licensed for the manufacture of medicinal products. (#In the UK, the MHRA and VMD have approved one year of practical experience for pharmacists). The MHRA advises that experience obtained in an establishment that has only a Specials Licence, or experience of the manufacture of active pharmaceutical ingredients, cannot contribute to the practical experience requirement (unless the site holds a manufacturer's licence) (Article 40 of 2001/83/EC). The applicant must demonstrate a thorough core competence in the manufacturing processes and the quality management systems involved in the production, testing, batch release and approval for sale of the products made under the Manufacturer's Licence(s) under which he or she is claiming his or her qualifying experience.

2. In addition, it is important that the applicant can demonstrate an ability to translate and extrapolate the working knowledge and understanding gained from his or her experience. In particular, scenario questions may be used to determine whether an applicant is able to articulate a logical approach to a practical situation with which he or she may be unfamiliar, thereby demonstrating his or her ability to apply his or her knowledge and experience. The applicant can expect detailed questioning on his or her knowledge of QMS principles, and will be required to demonstrate this by reference to the products or processes operating under the Manufacturer's Licence(s) under which he or she is claiming his or her qualifying experience. The assessors may

ask questions pertinent to other activities or functions which they consider relevant. The assessors must satisfy themselves that the applicant, after a suitable induction period, will be able to function as a Qualified Person in any licensed undertaking.

5.0 Role of the Qualified Person

5.1 Directives 2001/83/EC and 2001/82/EC

The functions of a Qualified Person as set out in the UK Statutory Instruments and EU Directives 2001/83/EC and 2001/82/EC are as follows:

- to ensure that each batch of the medicinal product to which the licence relates has been manufactured or assembled and checked in compliance with the provisions of the Act and Regulations made there under, the provisions of the Manufacturer's Licence and the provisions of the Product Licence or Marketing Authorisation which relates to the product;

- to certify in a register, or other record appropriate for the purpose, whether each production batch of the medicinal product to which the licence or authorisation relates satisfies the requirements set out above and to ensure that such register or other record is regularly maintained, in particular that the appropriate entries in such register or other record are made as soon as practicable after each such batch has been manufactured;

- for medicinal products manufactured outside the European Community, the Qualified Person must ensure that each imported batch has undergone in a Member State a full qualitative analysis, a quantitative analysis of at least all the active substances and all the other tests or checks necessary to ensure the quality of medicinal products in accordance with the requirements of the Marketing Authorisation (although it should be recognised that there are exemptions to this requirement: batches of medicinal products which have undergone such controls in a Member State shall be exempt from the above controls);

- in the case of medicinal products imported from a third country, where appropriate arrangements have been made by the Community with the exporting country to ensure that the manufacturer of the medicinal product applies standards of GMP at least equivalent to those laid down by the Community and to ensure that the controls referred to above have been carried out in the exporting country, the Qualified Person may be relieved of responsibility for carrying out those controls.

5.2 Directive 2001/20/EC

The functions of a Qualified Person as set out in the Clinical Trials Directive 2001/20/EC are as follows:

For IMP manufactured in the Member State concerned, that each batch of medicinal product has;

- been manufactured and checked in compliance with the requirements of Directive 2003/94/EC laying down the principles of good manufacturing practice for medicinal products for human use and investigational medicinal products for human use, the product specification file and the information notified pursuant to article 9(2) of Directive 2001/20/EC;

- in the case of an investigational medicinal product manufactured in a third country, that each production batch of product has been manufactured and checked in accordance with standards of good manufacturing practice at least equivalent to those laid down in Directive 2003/94/EC, in accordance with the product specification file and that each production batch has been checked in accordance with the information notified pursuant to article 9(2) of Directive 2001/20/EC;

- in the case of an investigational medicinal product which is a comparator product from a third country and which has a Marketing Authorisation, where the documentation certifying that each production batch has been manufactured in conditions at least equivalent to those laid down in Directive 2003/94/EC, that each production batch has undergone all relevant analyses, test or checks necessary to confirm its quality in accordance with information notified pursuant to article 9(2) of Directive 2001/20/EC. The role of the Qualified Person is thus of considerable importance within the industry and this should be reflected in the calibre of applicant appointed to such a position. Although every person included in the Register meets, in the opinion of the professional body concerned, the statutory requirements to become a Qualified Person, it is up to individual companies to satisfy themselves of the suitability of any individual applicant for a particular post. The Licensing Authority is the final arbiter of who can be named as a Qualified Person on a Manufacturer's Licence.

In Summary, the applicant must demonstrate:

- the relevant practical experience in one or more licensed facilities;

- an in-depth working knowledge and understanding, allied to practical experience;

- a thorough understanding of the principles and requirements laid out in "the Orange Guide";

- an ability to translate those principles and requirements to other situations currently outside his or her direct experience;

- an endorsement of his or her credentials, including qualifications and experience, from a sponsor.

2. Competencies for practicing pharmacist as identified by pharmaceutical society of Great Britain

The Royal Pharmaceutical Society identifies four clusters of competencies for practicing Pharmacists. The clusters and their subcomponents are as follows.

Cluster 1 | Patient and Pharmaceutical Care – focuses on our commitment to patient care and the provision of medicines.

Cluster 2 | Professional Practice – identifies support, practice guidance and professional support tools.

Cluster 3 | Personal Practice – relates to development and developing one"s own practice.

Cluster 4 | Management and Organisation – relates to leadership and service delivery.

CLUSTER 1 | PATIENT AND PHARMACEUTICAL CARE

- Patient consultation
- Need for the medicine
- Provision of medicine
- Selection of the medicine
- Medicine specific issues
- Medicines information and patient education
- Monitoring medicine therapy
- Evaluation of outcomes
- Transfer of care

CLUSTER 2 | PROFESSIONAL PRACTICE

2.1 Professionalism

2.2 Organization

2.3 Effective communication skills

2.4 Team work

2.5 Education and training

CLUSTER 3 | PERSONAL PRACTICE

3.1 Gathering information

3.2 Knowledge

3.3 Analyzing information

3.4 Providing information

3.5 Follow up

3.6 Research and evaluation

CLUSTER 4 | MANAGEMENT AND ORGANIZATION

4.1 Clinical governance

4.2 Service provision

4.3 Organizations

4.4 Budget and reimbursement.

4.5 Procurement

4.6 Staff management

3. Competencies of general, hospital, community pharmacists and pre-registration tutors

The competences provided here are intended to be a starting point. Some will have direct relevance and some will not.

GENERAL COMPETENCES FOR PHARMACISTS

These are a collection of competences that might apply to pharmacists working in any sector of practice and in any specialism. They are not core competences, ie they will not all be applicable to everyone.

Overview of the competency areas

G1   Being a pharmacist

G2   Interacting, and working with, people

G3   Being personally effective

G4   Being a manager

G5   Upholding quality and continuous improvement

G6   Helping others to learn and develop

G7   Making decisions and solving problems

G8   Working with information

G9   Participating in research and development

G10   Ensuring health and safety

G1 Being a pharmacist

Competences within this area

G1a   Using expert knowledge and skills to benefit patients

G1b   Using expert knowledge and skills to assist other healthcare professionals

G1c   Giving informed and accurate pharmaceutical advice

G1d   Taking a patient-centred approach

G1e   Making sound decisions and solving problems in relation to drug therapy

G1f   Using clinical and pharmaceutical knowledge to optimise the balance among effectiveness, safety and cost of medicines

G1g   Working within professional and organisational standards

G1h   Complying with pharmacy legislation, ethics and regulatory body policies

G1i   Working within boundaries of own professional expertise

G1j   Applying knowledge of the NHS and working according to NHS systems

G1k   Taking responsibility for the delivery of a pharmacy service to patients

G1l   Acting with professional autonomy

G1m   Keeping abreast of issues affecting pharmacy and pharmacists

G1n   Maintaining awareness of political, economic and managerial aspects of healthcare

G1o   Implementing national priorities

G1p   Implementing and supporting policy on health education

G1q   Promoting health and healthy lifestyles

G1r   Sourcing and providing good quality medicinal products

G1s   Recognising the contribution of, and collaborating with, other healthcare professionals

G1t   Working across professional and organisational boundaries

G1u   Working with sectors other than healthcare

G1v   Signposting to other services

G1w   Taking on new roles or responsibilities

G2 Interacting, and working with, people

Competences within this area

G2a   Demonstrating inter-personal skills, irrespective of the situation or the other person/people involved

G2b   Demonstrating presentation skills

G2c   Taking account of special communication needs in some circumstances

G2d   Recognising barriers to communication

G2e   Being assertive

G2f   Treating all people with respect

G2g   Leading teams and engendering common purpose

G2h   Working to develop and maintain team relationships (pharmacy and inter-professional)

G2i   Positively influencing individuals and organisations

G2j   Negotiating effectively

G2k   Minimising and resolving conflict
G2l   Being supportive and motivational
G2m   Maintaining and protecting privacy and confidentiality
G2n   Utilising the skills and knowledge of others
G2o   Responding to requests for advice or information

G3 Being personally effective

Competences within this area

G3a   Taking responsibility for own actions
G3b   Reflecting on own performance and taking responsibility for self-development
G3c   Recognising own limitations and referring to others when appropriate
G3d   Working with confidence
G3e   Being flexible
G3f   Being self-motivated and self-reliant
G3g   Setting and achieving personal and professional objectives
G3h   Thinking broadly and outside traditional boundaries
G3i   Being organised
G3j   Managing time and prioritising
G3k   Managing workload
G3l   Coping with pressure and stress
G3m   Being reliable
G3n   Showing initiative
G3o   Showing innovation
G3p   Showing, or sharing, vision

G4 Being a manager

Competences within this area

G4a   Showing reasoning and judgement to manage situations
G4b   Managing physical resources*
         * see G2 and G6 for aspects of managing people
G4c   Managing finances
G4d   Managing projects and activities
G4e   Managing and facilitating change
G4f   Overcoming obstacles in a changing environment
G4g   Seeing opportunities for change and development
G4h   Planning own work

G4i   Planning work activities for a team

G4j   Delegating appropriately

G4k   Facilitating and encouraging the use of skill mix

G4l   Planning strategically

G4m   Recruiting and selecting staff

G4n   Succession and contingency planning

G5 Upholding quality and continuous improvement

Competences within this area

G5a   Participating in professional audit

G5b   Sharing and adopting good practice

G5c   Adhering to standards of practice

G5d   Developing standards of practice, protocols and operating procedures

G5e   Adopting a reflective approach to practice

G5f   Complying with non-pharmacy legislation related to own sphere of practice, e.g. laws related to data protection, employment, discrimination

G5g   Implementing, or contributing to, the clinical governance agenda

G5h   Identifying and managing risk

G5i   Applying the principles of quality assurance to own practice

G5j   Challenging current practice

G5k   Responding to complaints

G6 Helping others to learn and develop

Competences within this area

G6a   Supporting and advising others in their development

G6b   Developing effective learning environments and learner support systems

G6c   Helping others to take responsibility for their own learning

G6d   Setting objectives and planning with learners

G6e   Contributing to the design and planning of learning activities

G6f   Teaching or training

G6g   Creating and using coaching opportunities

G6h   Supervising others

G6i   Taking account of learners' needs and learning styles

G6j   Using learning technologies appropriate to the context of the teaching/training

G6k   Monitoring and evaluating own teaching/training

G6l   Being a positive role model

G6m   Being a mentor

G6n   Facilitating others' CPD

G6o   Linking education/training with practice

G6p   Providing learners with opportunities to demonstrate their skills and knowledge

G6q   Promoting self-appraisal

G6r   Assessing others' knowledge

G6s   Assessing others' performance

G6t   Providing constructive feedback

G6u   Reviewing others' progress

G7 Making decisions and solving problems

Competences within this area

G7a   Identifying the exact nature of a problem

G7b   Identify key information and options to resolve the problem

G7c   Using suitable approaches to resolve specific problems

G7d   Making sound decisions after analysing information and options

G7e   Following up to ensure a problem is resolved

G8 Working with information

Competences within this area

G8a   Obtaining relevant and up-to-date information

G8b   Using a variety of information sources

G8c   Recognising when an information source is not suitable or reliable

G8d   Using a variety of information retrieval techniques

G8e   Evaluating information to identify key points and discard irrelevant and poor information

G8f   Applying evaluated information to practice

G8g   Sharing information

G8h   Ensuring the quality of information provided

G8i   Recording data and information so that retrieval of key material is easily possible

G8j   Manipulating data to extract key information

G8k   Taking account of the limitations of information technology

G8l   Using information technology

G9 Participating in research and development

Competences within this area

G9a   Demonstrating critical evaluation skills

G9b   Identifying gaps in the evidence base

G9c   Identifying research needs in the workplace

G9d   Generating or creating evidence

G9e   Developing and evaluating research protocols

G9f   Applying research evidence in practice

G9g   Supervising others in their research

G9h   Establishing research partnerships

G9i   Developing the service

G9j   Participating in the development of healthcare policy

G10 Ensuring health and safety

Competences within this area

G10a   Complying with health and safety legislation

G10b   Adopting safe working practices

G10c   Accepting shared responsibility for the safety of the working environment

COMPETENCES FOR PHARMACISTS WORKING IN COMMUNITY PRACTICE

Overview of the competency areas

C1 Working with patients and the public to maximise the efficacy, safety and cost-effectiveness of medicines

C2   Working with patients and the public to promote health

C3   Addressing the health and medication needs of specific client groups

C4   Working with other professions in healthcare and with other sectors

C5   Working according to the NHS contract

C6   Supplying medicines, dressings and appliances; and managing stock

C7   Working in a business context

C1 Working with patients and the public to maximise the efficacy, safety and cost-effectiveness of medicines

Competences within this area

C1a   Assessing the medication needs of patients

C1b   Reviewing medication for its clinical appropriateness

C1c   Reviewing medication with patients to identify difficulties and potential risk, eg concordance issues, adverse effects, changing medication needs

C1d   Monitoring indicators of disease progress, drug efficacy or drug toxicity

C1e   Providing a pharmaceutical service to patients in their home

C1f   Providing advice and counselling, eg related to minor ailments, medicines for purchase, appliances, self-care

C1g   Participating in referral schemes to treat minor ailments

C1h   Undertaking clinical audit

C1i   Generating and maintaining records of medication supplied to patients

C1j   Recording and reporting adverse drug reactions

C1k   Documenting pharmaceutical care plans

C1l   Producing and providing practice leaflets containing information about services available

C2 Working with patients and the public to promote health

Competences within this area

C2a   Providing information to promote public health and prevent disease

C2b   Participating in national and local health campaigns and initiatives

C2c   Creating and making use of opportunities to encourage healthy lifestyles

C2d   Providing a smoking cessation service

C2e   Screening and testing for chronic conditions

C2f   Providing advice in relation to self-testing

C3 Addressing the health and medication needs of specific client groups

Competences within this area

C3a   Addressing the medication needs of patients transferring from one health/social care setting to another

C3b   Providing pharmaceutical care to the elderly and their carers

C3c   Providing pharmaceutical care to children and their carers

C3d   Providing pharmaceutical care to patients who require palliative care in their own homes

C3e   Providing pharmaceutical care to people with chronic conditions, eg asthma, diabetes, CHD, mental ill health

C3f   Providing pharmaceutical care to people with specific dietary needs

C3g   Providing services to drug misusers, including supervised administration and needle exchange

C3h   Providing pharmaceutical care to people who use surgical appliances, hosiery and medical gases

C4 Working with other professions in healthcare and with other sectors

Competences within this area

C4a   Acting on referrals from GPs and NHS Direct

C4b   Providing medicines-related information to other healthcare professionals

C4c   Providing training and education to other healthcare professionals

C4d   Evaluating drug information to assist other professionals

C4e   Participating in the development and review of patient group directions, treatment protocols, formularies and guidelines

C4f   Evaluating and reviewing medicines use and utilisation

C4g   Working across professional boundaries

C4h   Providing training and education to pharmacy staff

C4i   Analysing and reviewing repeat prescribing

C4j   Providing a pharmaceutical service to care homes, including intermediate care, and to hospices

C4k   Signposting to other healthcare or social care provision

C5 Working according to the NHS contract

Competences within this area

C5a   Understanding, and working in accordance with, NHS terms of service and contract, including specifications of the Drug Tariff

C5b   Analysing and evaluating prescribing data

C5c   Developing and implementing new services under local or national contracts

C5d   Participating in local accreditation schemes

C5e   Providing services out of hours

C5f   Premises design for dispensing and consulting services

C6 Supplying medicines, dressings and appliances; and managing stock

Competences within this area

C6a   Dispensing / managing the dispensing process

C6b   Providing a repeat dispensing service

C6c   Providing collection and delivery services

C6d   Providing an emergency hormonal contraception service

C6e   Supplying oxygen

C6f   Managing stock, including correct storage

C6g   Disposing of medication and participating in medication disposal schemes

C7 Working in a business context

Competences within this area

C7a   Analyse basic business problems, assess alternative choices, and propose actions

C7b   Present, summarise, interpret and analyse economic and business data

C7c   Buying and selling

C7d   Marketing services and products to identified customer groups

C7e   Premises design to meet business needs

Competences for pharmacists working in hospital practice

Produced with reference to the 2001 Audit Commission report A Spoonful of Sugar: medicines management in NHS hospitals and the 1996 NHS Scotland report Clinical Pharmacy in the hospital pharmaceutical service: a framework for practice

Overview of the competency areas

HP1   Planning pharmaceutical care for individual patients

HP2   Providing medicines information and advice

HP3   Promoting the safety, efficacy and cost-effectiveness of medicines

HP4   Monitoring prescriptions

HP5   Identifying and managing risk to patients

HP6   Optimising medicines administration

HP7   Promoting health

HP8   Evaluating medicines use

HP9   Managing transfer to another healthcare setting

HP10   Promoting quality and improving practice

HP11   Managing formularies, guidelines and protocols

HP12   Working across professional and organisational boundaries

HP13   Reviewing and developing services

HP14   Producing, using and maintaining records; using information technology

HP15   Undertaking specialised activities

HP1 Planning pharmaceutical care for individual patients

Competences within this area

HP1a   Assessing the individual patient's pharmaceutical needs

HP1b   Conducting a structured patient interview

HP1c   Compiling a medication history/medication profile

HP1d   Taking account of the patient's medication history/profile and clinical records

HP1e   Taking account of risk factors (w.r.t. the patient and the medication)

HP1f   Liaising with other members of the patient's healthcare team

HP1g   Selecting, or advising on, suitable medication, dose, route, frequency, timing and duration

HP1h   Monitoring the patient's progress and outcomes

HP1i   Reviewing, monitoring and updating the pharmaceutical care plan

HP1j   Recording the pharmaceutical care plan and the advice given to the patient and members of the healthcare team

HP2 Providing medicines information and advice

Competences within this area

HP2a   Keeping up-to-date with new products and therapeutic advances

HP2b   Anticipating and identifying the need for evaluated drug information to support formulary review or individual patient care

HP2c   Establishing the background to requests for drug information and advice from healthcare professionals and patients

HP2d   Participating in the education and training of other healthcare professionals

HP2e   Advising on the legal and ethical considerations of using medicines in ways which are not covered by a product licence

HP2f   Liaising with others in regard to clinical trials in progress in the ward or unit

HP2g   Providing advice on pharmaceutical aspects of clinical trial design, eg to research and ethical committees

HP3 Promoting the safety, efficacy and cost-effectiveness of medicines

Competences within this area

HP3a   Reviewing prescribing

HP3b   Reviewing patients' medication, eg on admission

HP3c   Educating and training other healthcare professionals on the safe and effective use of medicines

HP3d   Training, advising and counselling patients and carers in medicines taking

HP3e   Educating groups, eg patient groups, school children

HP3f   Providing information leaflets and other written information

HP3g   Assessing and prioritising the education and counselling needs of patients

HP3h   Monitoring patients' understanding of information provided

HP3i   Recording education and counselling activities

HP3j   Training other healthcare staff to provide education and counselling on the use of medicines and appliances

HP3k   Involving patients and carers in the audit of education and counselling services

HP3l   Assessing future medicines cost pressures

HP4 Monitoring prescriptions

Competences within this area

HP4a   Ensuring that the medication prescribed, and the dose, route, frequency, timing and duration, are all appropriate to the patient and their diagnosis

HP4b   Ensuring that the prescription is complete, unambiguous and legal

HP4c   Ensuring that the treatment is not duplicated by pharmacologically similar drugs

HP4d   Ensuring that there are no incompatibilities, interactions allergies or intolerance

HP4e   Ensuring that the prescription complies with relevant formularies and prescribing policies

HP4f   Ensuring that a new prescription is written when treatment is altered

HP4g   Discussing necessary amendments with the prescriber and securing their agreement

HP4h   Recording actions taken in the prescription monitoring process

HP4i   Recording outcomes

HP5 Identifying and managing risk to patients

Competences within this area

HP5a   Ensuring that prescribing for individual patients takes account of predictable adverse effects

HP5b   Ensuring that unnecessary drug use is avoided

HP5c   Individualising drug dosage requirements

HP5d   Identifying risk factors specific to the patient, eg their characteristics; social, environmental, functional, cognitive; aspects of their disease

HP5e   Identifying risk factors in relation to the patient's medication, eg toxicity, availability, bioavailability, administration issues

HP5f   Ensuring that patients receive cautionary and advisory labels and appropriate counselling in relation to the use of their medication

HP5g   Identifying patients who will require close monitoring of their medicines administration

HP5h   Educating and training pharmacy staff and other healthcare staff on the prevention, detection and reporting of ADRs

HP5i   Monitoring patients for adverse reactions, including delayed effects

HP5j   Participating in therapeutic drug monitoring

HP5k   Using all sources of information that may be helpful in detecting and monitoring ADRs

HP5l   Reporting, and encouraging others to report, ADRs

HP5m Monitoring patients for iatrogenic disease

HP6 Optimising medicines administration

Competences within this area

HP6a   Ensuring medication is administered correctly

HP6b   Developing/managing self-administration schemes

HP6c   Training staff involved in the administration of medicines

HP7 Promoting health

Competences within this area

HP7a   Providing health education information

HP7b   Promoting healthy lifestyles and increasing awareness of current issues and guidelines

HP7c   Screening for chronic conditions

HP7d   Planning and managing vaccination and immunisation programmes

HP7e   Participating in measures to minimise the spread of communicable diseases, eg in relation to travellers, sexual practices, drug misuse

HP7f   Contributing to health protection initiatives

HP8 Evaluating medicines use

Competences within this area

HP8a   Identifying medicines which are suitable for medicines use evaluation

HP8b   Defining acceptable standards for medicines use, with objective and measurable criteria

HP8c   Measuring and documenting outcomes against the standards

HP8d   Reporting results of medicines use evaluation to the clinical team

HP8e   Recommending actions as a result of medicines use evaluation

HP9 Managing transfer to another healthcare setting

Competences within this area

HP9a   Collaborating with professionals to whom responsibility for the patient is to be transferred

HP9b   Taking account of shared care protocols

HP9c   Ensuring the patient receives appropriate counselling and advice on discharge

HP9d   Writing/reviewing the discharge prescription

HP9e   Reviewing the pharmaceutical care plan for the patient

HP9f   Making arrangements for the necessary medicines, dressings and appliances to be supplied on time

HP9g   Documenting the discharge/transfer and pharmaceutical care plans

HP9h   Transferring information between the healthcare settings

HP10 Promoting quality and improving practice

Competences within this area

HP10a   Contributing to the clinical governance agenda

HP10b   Managing risk

HP10c   Managing/embracing change

HP10d   Utilising the skills of other staff (skill mix)

HP10e   Training and developing staff

HP10f   Adopting reflective practice

HP10g   Recognising responsibility and accountability

HP10h   Taking an evidence-based approach to practice

HP10i   Taking account of National Service Frameworks

HP10j   Undertaking Continuing Professional Development

HP10k   Participating in professional audit

HP10l   Participating in clinical audit

HP10m   Participating in peer review

HP10n   Accepting performance review

HP10o   Undertaking performance review of staff

HP10p   Reducing medication errors

HP10q   Learning from errors

HP10r   Contributing to the development of quality standards

HP11   Managing formularies, guidelines and protocols Competences within this area

HP11a   Developing formularies, guidelines and protocols in liaison with medical staff, nursing staff and other pharmacy colleagues

HP11b   Ensuring that stocks of medicines held in treatment areas conform to the formulary

HP11c   Ensuring that procedures are in place for the supply of formulary and non-formulary items

HP11d   Reviewing formularies, guidelines and protocols in collaboration with medical, nursing and pharmacy staff

HP11e   Ensuring that deviation from a formulary, clinical guideline or treatment protocol is the result of an active decision which involves the pharmacist

HP12 Working across professional and organisational boundaries

Competences within this area

HP12a   Working/liaising with primary care

HP12b   Providing support to prescribers, eg reviewing repeat prescribing

HP12c   Using and contributing to shared records

HP12d   Providing intermediate care services

HP12e   Providing palliative care services, eg to hospices

HP12f   Developing joint care protocols

HP12g   Working with NHS agencies

HP12h   Working with sectors other than healthcare

HP13 Reviewing and developing services

Competences within this area

HP13a   Reviewing services

HP13b   Developing new services

HP13c   Developing 'whole system' prescribing

HP13d   Redesigning processes

HP13e   Redesigning medicines supply, eg original pack dispensing, automation

HP13f   Improving procurement systems

HP14 Producing, using and maintaining records; using information technology

Competences within this area

HP14a   Using information technology, eg electronic records

HP14b   Compiling information on patients' current and past drug treatments

HP14c   Documenting a medication history/profile

HP14d   Reviewing and maintaining medication records

HP14e   Recording clinical interventions

HP15 Undertaking specialised activities

Competences within this area

HP15a   Supplementary prescribing (see separate competences for supplementary prescribers)

HP15b   Participating in, or running, outpatient clinics

HP15c   Producing aseptic and cytotoxic products in a specialised unit

HP15d   Preparing sterile and non-sterile products extemporaneously in a licensed production unit

HP15e   Managing an aseptic or production unit

HP15f   Working in, or running, a quality assurance service

HP15g   Preparing products for clinical trials

HP15h   Preparing radiopharmaceuticals

Competences for preregistration tutors

PT1 Being a role model

Competences within this area

PT1a   Working to high professional and ethical standards

PT1b   Maintaining a patient-centred focus

PT1c   Maintaining a broad perspective; keeping abreast of professional and wider healthcare issues

PT1d   Reflecting on performance and undertaking professional development

PT1e   Managing time and prioritising

PT2 Being a people manager

Competences within this area

PT2a   Communicating at all levels

PT2b   Treating all team members with respect

PT2c   Engendering common purpose amongst the work team

PT2d   Utilising the skills and knowledge of others

PT3 Being a trainer and coach

Competences within this area

PT3a   Supporting and advising others in their development

PT3b   Empowering others to take responsibility for their own learning

PT3c   Setting objectives with learners and planning training

PT3d   Creating and using coaching opportunities

PT3e   Taking account of learners' needs and learning styles

PT3f   Encouraging self-appraisal

PT3g   Providing feedback

PT4 Being an assessor

Competences within this area

PT4a   Providing learners with opportunities to demonstrate their competence

PT4b   Assessing diverse sources of evidence

PT4c   Reviewing progress

DEFINITIONS

- **Accreditation:** the process whereby an association or agency grants public recognition to ar organization, site or program that meets certain established qualifications or standards, as determined through initial and periodic evaluations.

- **Active learning:** a process or methodology whereby learners are actively engaged in the learning process, rather than "passively" absorbing lectures. Active learning involves reading, writing, discussion, and engagement in solving problems, analysis, synthesis, and evaluation.

- **Administrators:** senior personnel with organizational and leadership positions in the school or institution.

- **Approval:** official endorsement attesting to conformity to set standards and requirements. (Similar term: Recognition)

- **Assessment:** a test or measure of knowledge, skills, performance, achievement or learning for or in a specific area or process.

- **Assessment:** Assessment is one or more processes, carried out by the institutions that identify, collect and prepare data to evaluate the achievement of the PEOs and POs.

- **Competence:** the ability to perform one's duties accurately and confidently, make correct judgments, and interact appropriately with patients and with colleagues. Professional competence is characterized by good problem-solving and decision-making abilities, a strong knowledge base, and the ability to apply knowledge and experience to diverse patient-care situations.

- **Competencies:** the knowledge, skills, behaviours and attitudes that an individual accumulates, develops, and acquires through education, training, and work experience.

- **Continuing Education (CE):** a structured process of education designed or intended to support the continuous development of pharmacists to maintain and enhance their professional competence.

- **Continuing Professional Development (CPD):** the responsibility of individual pharmacists for systematic maintenance, development and broadening of knowledge, skills and attitudes, to ensure continuing competence as a professional throughout their careers.

- **Continuous Quality Improvement (CQI):** an internally driven management strategy and approach that aims to constantly improve quality by: identifying current and future desired outcomes; adopting relatively continuous assessments and evaluations of performance and achievement; identifying potential causes of quality defects; taking appropriate action to avoid or correct deficiencies; implementing process improvements and innovations; and evaluating the impact of all interventions.

- **Course outcomes (COs):** These are narrower statements that describe what students are expected to know, and be able to at the end of each course.
- **Credential:** documented evidence of professional or educational qualifications (examples include: degree, diploma, and certification).
- **Criteria:** (see Standard)
- **Educational Outcomes:** the intended quantifiable and measurable results (such as knowledge or skills) that should be achieved on completion of a course or program of study.
- **Evaluation:** Evaluation is one of more process, done by the evaluation team for interpreting the data and evidence accumulated through assessment objectives. Evaluation determines the extent to which PEOs or POs are being achieved, and results in decisions and actions to improve the program.
- **Evaluation:** the forming of a judgment based on the collection. analysis and interpretation of data from process and outcome measures with a view to determining the quality of one or more activities and the achievement of desired outcomes.
- **Faculty:** the professors, teachers, and lecturers of a university, college or school.
- **License:** a credential issued by a government or regulatory body that inadicates that the holder is in compliance with minimum mandatory requirements necessary to practice in a particular profession or occupation. (Similar term: Registration)
- **Lifelong Learning:** all learning that occurs during the career of a practitioner, (including structured educational programs oractivities, training. informal or unstructured learning, and work-based learning) that aims to improve knowledge, skills and competencies.
- **Mapping:** Mapping is the process of representing, preferably in a matrix form, the correlation among the parameters. It may be done for one to many. many to one and many to many parameters.
- **Mission:** the fundamental purpose, objective, or reason to exist (raison d'Otre) for an organization or institution, which guides its planning and activities.
- **Outcome:** something that s achieved or results from an activity or series of activities
- **Practice Experience:** a structured or semi-structured teaching and learning activity that takes place in a practice setting and involves real-life situations and inter-

personal interactions. (Similar terms: Practice-based Learning, Experiential Education, Clinical Experience)

- **Practice Site:** a healthcare delivery setting (such as a community pharmacy or hospital) in which students undertake practice experiences.

- **Preceptor:** a practitionerwhoteaches (in a structured orsemi-structured fashion) and supervises students in his or her professional practice setting. (Similar term: Practitioner-educator, Clinical Instructor)

- **Professionalism:** The [demonstration of] ethics, attitudes, values, qualities, conduct, and behaviors that characterize a profession and are expected of its practitioners.

- **Program Educational Objectives (PEOs):** These are broad statements that describe the career and professional accomplishments that the program is preparing graduates to achieve.

- **Program outcomes (POs):** These are narrower statements that describe what students are expected to know and be able to do upon the graduation.

- **Programmatic Outcomes:** the broad range of deliverables (results or products) that an organized and cohesive group of activities (a program) produces.

- **Quality Assurance:** the systematic review of educational programmes to ensure that acceptable standards of education, scholarship and infrastructure are being maintained.

- **Recognition:** (see Approval)

- **Registered:** Adjective used to describe a pharmacist who has met requirements for licensure or registration and whose name has been entered on a registry of practitioners who are licensed or registered to practice in that jurisdiction.

- **Rubric:** A rubric articulates the expectations for students' performance. It is a set of criteria for assessing students' work or performance.

- **Scope of practice:** the range of professional tasks and functions that a practitioner can perform as specified by legislation, rules, or regulations; the boundaries within which a practitioner may practice.

- **Staff:** administrative and other support personnel in an office, organization, or institution.

- **Stakeholder:** any individual, group, or organization that has an interest or involvement in a particular activity, set of activities or outcome.

- **Standard:** something set up and established by authority as a rule for measure of quality; the basis for a decision or judgment of quality. (Similar terms: Criterion/Criteria)

- **Substantive change:** A major or substantial change in a school or its educational program. Examples - incluce: any change in the established mission or goals of the school or institution; the addition or deletion of courses, pathway or programs that represent a significant departure in either content or method of delivery; a substantial change in enrollment; a substiantial change in the number of clock or credit hours requried for successful complition of the program; a significant charge in the length of the program; and the establishment of an additional geographic location at which the program is offered.

REFERENCE

1. National Board of Accreditation (NBA). Accreditation manual for Pharmacy UG programs. New Delhi: NBA; 2013.

2. Sanjaya Mishra. Quality Assurance in Higher Education An introduction. Bangalore: National Assessment and Accreditation Council (NAAC) and Commonwealth of Learning (COL); 2006

3. D. Brahadeeswaran, M.A. Abdul Hakeem. A Review of NBA's Accreditation Criteria for Bachelor's Degree Programs in Engineering. J. Engg. Sc. Mgmt. Ed. 2012; 5(2):475-9

4. R Krishna Murthy. Accreditation - the role of Universities, AICTE & NBA. Proceedings of First World Summit on Accreditation; 2012 Mar. 25-29; New Delhi, India. New Delhi: NBA; 2012.

5. S. B. Bhise. Accreditation of Pharmacy Institutions: Background and the new norms. Indian J. Pharm. Edu. Res. 2013;47(2):188-92.

6. S. B. Bhise & A. M. Deshpande. Accreditation of Pharmacy Institutions: Evaluation Criteria. Indian J. Pharm. Edu. Res. 2014; 48(1):1–5

7. S. B. Bhise & A. M. Deshpande. Accreditation of Pharmacy Institutions: Design of Curriculum Indian J. Pharm. Edu. Res. 2014; 48(4):1–5

8. Accreditation council for pharmacy education accreditation standards and guidelines for the professional program in pharmacy leading to the doctor of pharmacy degree adopted: January 15, 2006 released: February 17, 2006 effective: July 1, 2007

9. Accreditation standards and key elements for the professional program in pharmacy leading to the doctor of pharmacy degree draft standards 2016 released 2/3/2014

10. Accreditation Standards and Guidelines for the Professional Program in Pharmacy leading to the Doctor of Pharmacy; effective from July, 2007; Accreditation Council for Pharmacy Education, Chicago, Illinois; 2006.

11. Accreditation Council for Pharmacy Education; Standards 2007; Self-study Guide; 2007.

12. A Global Framework for Quality Assurance of Pharmacy Education; FIP Pharmacy Education Taskforce; 2008.

13. 12. National Competency Standards Framework for Pharmacists in Australia, Pharmaceutical Society of Australia, 2010.

14.   Clinical Pharmacist Competencies; ACCP White Paper; Pharmacotherapy; 2008; 28(6); 806-815.

15.   RPS Foundation Pharmacy Framework; A framework for professional development in foundation practice across pharmacy; Royal Pharmaceutical Society; 2014.

16.   A Global Competency Framework for Services Provided by Pharmacy Workforce; FIP Pharmacy Education Taskforce; 2010.

17.   Identifying & Defining Competencies; Pharmine; Pharmacy Education in Europe; 2011.

18.   Competencies for Pharmacists; Continuous Professional Development; Royal Pharmaceutical Society; 2001.

INDEX